GERRY HILL

To. A dear friend Rose
from Bridget Richards
Hope U will love
my book
Peace + Love
Always
Bridie

BRIDGET RICHARDS

GERRY HILL

Matador
9 De Montfort Mews
Leicester LE1 7FW, UK
Tel: (+44) 116 255 9311 / 9312
Email: books@troubador.co.uk
Web: www.troubador.co.uk/matador

ISBN 1 905237-21-9

Cover illustration: ??????

Typeset in 11pt Plantin Light by Troubador Publishing Ltd, Leicester, UK

Matador is an imprint of Troubador Publishing Ltd

CONTENTS

Acknowledgements   vii

Introduction   viii

Famous Irish Names   ix

Family Tree   xiii

1   THE MIGRATION   1

2   ROMANTIC MEETINGS   5

3   DABBER   27

4   THE DEPRESSION (1930s)   31

5   HAPPY DAYS   48

6   PADDY'S MARKET   63

7   GRAN O' DONNELL   69

8   THE EVACUATION   79

9   CHRISTMAS TIME   91

10   RETURN TO ROOTS   97

ACKNOWLEDGEMENTS

I wish to express my sincere gratitude to these people who have assisted me to write this true story, The head Liberian from the central library in Dublin, for giving me permission to use the picture of 'The Potato Famine' for the front cover of this book also thanks to Etha Casey at Riversdale college, the priest in St Anthony's church, some of the stall holders in Paddy's market, Bill teacher in Rotunda for helping me with the computer, most of ail I am deeply grateful to my nephew Tom Slemen without his help I wouldn't have completed this novel, many thanks to my sister Mary, for providing me with all the family history, a very special thanks to Keith Birch in the Liverpool university.

INTRODUCTION

This is a true story, which was to change the lives of these people, they originate as far back to the years (1845–1847) some tales are sad some are happy and the rest are romantic.

A time to laugh
A time to cry
A time to sign
A time to die

FAMOUS IRISH NAMES

O' DONNELL ABU

The name of this great Tir Conail clan evokes the martial spirit of Ireland. The name of this great Tir - Conail evokes the martial spirit of Ireland. There are few names in Irish history, which convey a better recollection than that of O'Donnell a name that conjures up visions of the martial spirit of Ireland as embodied in the famous Hugh O'Donnell and other leaders of this great clan. Appropriately the name continues to hold a prominent place in Irish affairs in the persons of Mr Tom O'Donnell, a member of Dail Eirean and European Parliament an Pander O'Donnell veteran socialist and writer, in the sporting world, Wexford's Nick

O'DONNELL ABÚ

The name of this great Tir Conaill clan evokes the martial spirit of Ireland.

MR. TOM O'DONNELL

In hoc signo vinces

THE O'DONNELL ARMS

O'Donnell achieved fame for the name as All Ireland hurling star in the (1950s).

The principal O'Donnell clan belong where it was earliest known as the Cineal Conail of the tribe of Conal. This name they took from Conal Guiban, son of Nail of the nine hostages, monarch of Ireland from (379–406) A D.

The O'Donnell's were also known as the clan Dialog, the first of them to become chief of Tir-Conaff in the ninth century, it was from his son Donal that the name derived.

Caffer, the great grandson of this Donal, was the first to call himself O'Donnell. The territory of the O'Donnells, up to the close of the eleventh century, did not extend beyond the present barony of Kilmacrennen in Donagal, but in the early part of the thirteenth century, they were styled Lord of Tir Conail, Cineal Moe, Inishowen and Fermangh was later ceded to the Maguires.

The principal seat of the clan was Donegal Castle and its chief's were inaugurated on the rock of Doon at Kilmacrennan. Up to the close of the twelfth century the O' Cannons and O'Maidoreyes were chiefs of Tir-Conaill. The last representatives were Flaherry O'Mal-dorey, who died in (1197) and Rory O'Canannans who founded the Abbey of Assoe .

Donal Mor O'Donnell then became chief. His son, Geoffrey, who was compelled to defend himself against Roro Canannan, who in (1248) , sought to recover his patrimony. Geoffrey who won the date, was succeeded by his brother Donal Oge O'Donnell who after a turbulent reign of twenty - three years, was slain at the battle of Disert - da Crioch, now Disertcreagh, Co Tyrone.

His grandson Hugh did much to extend his possessions of the clan when he died in (1333) he styled Lord of Breffiny in edition to his other titles.

Turlough-an-Fions of the wine-became chief in (1393), and after a peaceable reign died in the habit of a monk in the Abbey of Assaroein (1422). His son Nail Gary, who succeeded him was taken prisoner by the English and died in captivity on the Isle of Man in (14390), Hugh Roe O'Donnell, who became chief of Tir-Conail in (14750.

A later chief, Manus O'Donnell was a great patron of literature and science. The best known of his works is 'The Life of Colum Cillie'. He was also the author of many love poems, having been thrice married, he would seem to have amorous poems, individual, in (1555) he was imprisoned by his son Calvaghin in the Castle of Liford, where he died in (1563).

Hugh O'Donnell, who was knighted by Sir Henry Sidney in (1567), was the father of the famed, Hugh Roe, or Red Hugh, also Rory, afterwards Earl of Tir-Conail, Calvag and Manus, Red Hugh who were fostered by O' Doherty and O'Cahan, from his early days gave promise to being one of the most powerful chiefs the clan ever had, and the Irish of Ulster looked to him as the destined deliverer of their country.

His reputation so worried the government that they had him imprisoned in Dublin Castle, where he remained for three years before escaping (1555), He crossed the Dublin mountains to the home of Felim O' Toole at Powers court, they were recaptured.

A year later he again escaped accompanied by Henry an Art O'Neal and they made their way in the snow to the O'Bryne country in Wicklow. The two O'Neils failed to survive the track.

The brave O'Donnell with his servant Turlough O' Hagan, were conveyed by Fiach Mac Hugh O'Bryne to the far side of Dublin, from which making their way through, Meath and Louth, they reached Dundannon, where Hugh O' Neil resided. On his arrival in Donagal, Red Hugh O' Donnell was inaugurated chief of the clan.

For years afterwards he led his clan in defending their territory against the incessant attacks of the English and their Irish allies, in (1594) he sent the Bishop of Killais to seek aid from the King of Spain. Two years later he received an emissary from Phillip third King of Spain to the Castle of Liffard and arranged and arranged to have supplies sent to him. O'Donnell was victorious in several subsequent battles, the most notable, being of The Yellow Ford, near Armagh.

In October (1800), news came of the landing of the Spaniards at Kinsdale O'Donnell immediately set out to meet them but here he met his first defeat by an English force. He then went to Spain where he died from poisoning, by an English agent. His body was interred with regal honours in the monastery of St Francis at Valladolld. In (1606) Roy, Earl of Tir-connall and Calvagh died in 1617).

Nail Gary O'Donnell by his son Manus, was ancestor of the O'Donnells of Newport, Co Mayo, and Hugh Buidie was the ancestor of the O'Donnell's of Larkfied.Co. Leitrim, and Greyfield, Co.Roscommon, Con Oge, brother of Naill Gary was ancestor of the O'Donnells of Castlebar, Austria and Spain.

FAMILY TREE

Grt. Granparents   Neal O' Donnell   *Farmer*
                         Born in County Mayo. West Ireland

Grt . Granparents   **Patrick O' Donnell**   *Farm labourer*
                      Born (1813)

                      MARRIED

                      Catherine Sodan
                      Born (1815) kitchen maid
                      Liverpool

                              * * * * *

Siblings   **Brigita**
             James   *Rope maker*
             Catherine
             Mary Ann
             Margaret
             all born in Liverpool

Grandparents   **Brigita O' Donnell**   *Tweeny*
                 Born (30-10-1860)

                 MARRIED

                 George Jones
                 Born in Tony Pandy South Wales

Siblings   **Harriet**

Julian
George
James

Grandparents   **William Wilkinson**   *Marine Fireman*
Born ?

MARRIED

Martha Wignal
Born Liverpool

Siblings   **William**
Daniel
Thomas
Martha
Margarita
Esther
Frances

My Parents   **George Jones**
Born (6-9-1895)

MARRIED

Margarita Wilkinson
Born (4-12-1998)

1

THE MIGRATION

The Great Potato Famine, was a national catastrophe that deci-mated the Irish–speaking population, it left over half a million people dead and dying from disease and starvation, there was a massive wave of migration to North America, Canada and Liverpool. The tragedy of the Great Famine played a very impor-tant political, cultural and literary role for Ireland and migrants migrated to Liverpool.

In the year (1847), the public works of Ireland started to close down the people began to suffer dreadfully they became quite desperate, thousands of them gathered outside the workhouses with their families, pleading to be taken in but the troops were called in and the crowds began to vanish for a while.

The poor creatures raised a terrible cry but there was no violence, first they could go along to the soup kitchens. Each person had to stand in an exceedingly very large, long queue that stretched for miles and miles, majority of them collapsed before it came to their turn, but those who could just about stand the long harsh ordeal, eventually when it came to their turn all they received was just a few ounces of rice mixed together with water added to it, plus a piece of bread which weighed only four ounces, the bread was made up with a of Indian meal.

The Irish folks main substantial food was potatoes, at that time there was a server potato famine sweeping through all Ireland, it was estimated that approximately two and a half million people had already starved to death in Ireland during that disastrous, millions of them did their utmost to migrate.

While they were desperately trying to climb on board, there was an avalanche, thousands of them lay dead or dying on the roadside, a great number of them were mostly women and children, the boats were only made of thin plywood, thousands of them contacted contagious diseases, they were screaming out for water, while hundreds of them were staggering, trying so hard to walk, the disease was "The Black Fever".

The patients limbs would begin to twitch violently, raving about delirium they would begin to vomit uncontrollably, they weren't able to control themselves, throwing their limbs all over, as the fever got worse, their body would start burning, then a rash would appear, then agonising sores would spread all over their body then down to their fingers and toes gangrene would then set in, the smell of their bodies was atrocious, the cabin was full of dead bodies and very ill and tormented dying people, they had no medical treatment at all.

On (June 1st 1847), the passenger act was tat all immigrants were to be medically examined, but the act was not carried out, the vessels could barely manage to crawl on to the shore, the poor folks were still screaming out for mercy, parched with thirst and dying with starvation and malnutrition, covered in lice, the poor little children, searching hopelessly to try and find their parents.

Thousands of them lay dying without any hope of surviving, dying with the Black Fever. As they had been fed on that terrible unbearable voyage was only pounds of provisions, barely sufficient to prevent them from destitution, crowds of them were women and children lying in the bitter sleet and snow with the fierce hailstones beating down upon their worn out bodies and stinging faces, half naked in the fields their fathers were trying so desperately hard to try and scrape food for them, the poor children were screaming out with server hunger and devouring the rotten turnips from their elders.

The report of the state of the destitute in the workhouse was horrific, the government had cancelled the issue of clothing, in the workhouses, females and males and children inmates in the wards lay half naked, they barely existed with just enough food to prevent them from starvation, fever and dysentery and an epidemic was very sever, in (1850), the figure was (270,000) that had contacted the terrible disease, the number was astounding as they were one eyed children.

Hundreds of children males and females even new born babies had the disease, they all lay huddled together without air, the water was unfit to drink and there where no washing facilities on board, lying cramped on filthy bunks.

By June Ist (1845–1847) it was estimated that (300,000) of them arrived in Liverpool, most of the passenger brokers tormented them, by wickedly deceiving them by displaying a loaf of bread on a table in their office where the poor migrants could clearly see it, they would delude them into thinking that they were going to be fed.

Penniless and wretched the Irish immigrants crept for shelter in disused cellars and other uninhabited places that they could manage to find, during that period the inhabited places of Liverpool were packed together, (40) of them living together in courts and basements that were built face to face and only nine feet apart, lacking in drainage they were evil smelling and totally airless, the poor folks who suffered the most were the Irish immigrants, in (1847), tens of thousands of them had arrived in Liverpool, the town police could not control them so (2,000) regular troops were brought in and camped in Liverpool.

Hundreds of the Irish immigrants went to live down b y the docks in the south-end the district was nick named "The Holy Land", because most of the streets down there have names of some of the prophets in the bible, after they all began to settle in they named it Gerry Hill.

They couldn't obtain work even if they had, they didn't have the strength to work as they were in no fit state after the terrible ordeal they had suffered, the women and children went begging on the streets while the men tried to make a shelter for their families, they were packed together in filthy slum dwellings that weren't even fit for animals, most of them that couldn't even walk lay dying or dangerously ill.

2
ROMANTIC MEETINGS

Patrick O'Donnell was my great grandfather, he was born in County Mayo in the west of Ireland.

Through the dreadful disaster of the Potato Famine, he decided to migrate to Liverpool, totally exhausted after a rigorous crossing, quenched with thirst and dying with hunger, fortunately for him he soon began to recover, he was a very strong man.

He settled down in Albert Street, Toxteth Park, after a while he met a pretty young lady named Margaret Sodan, they fell in love and became engaged later on they got married in St. Patrick's church in Park Place.

They went to live at No 4, Court. Fernie Street, Toxteth, as time went passed by, Margaret became pregnant, she gave birth to a beautiful baby girl who was christened Brigita, which means in Irish, The Fire Godess,later she was known to us as Gran O'Donnell, my loving Granma, who we called Gannie.

Three years after Margaret gave birth to a lovely baby boy, he was baptised James, then three years after Catherine was born, eleven years later Margaret Ellen was born, last of all came Mary Ann.

They went and rented a small terraced house in Rutter Street, down by the Holy Land, where they opened a cake shop in their front parlour, Patrick did the manual work while Margaret attended to the financial part and the baking, she baked sweet and savoury pies, scones, cookies, bread and bread pudding and lovely Irish bunloaf, that they sold at a very reasonable price to neighbours, friends and relatives, some folks were allowed tick, and to the poor, poor they gave them free of charge especially, on a Saturday afternoon just before closing time, they manage to survive quite well considering there was a recession going on during that period, majority of folks were living far below the breadline.

A few years later on a Christmas Eve, after their Mother had just finished preparing their Christmas dinner, she began to feel very tired so she decided to go and have a lie down in her bedroom, to regain her strength, sadly to say she passed away, it was such a terrible shock to her family, it broke their hearts.

Three years after their Mother's departure from this world, their Father remarried to, his daughter Brigita's girlfriend, his son James and his daughters were absolutely flabbergasted, they just couldn't accept the situation, they never stopped pinning for their dear Mother.

James was a professional rope- maker, he planned to leave home as soon as he could save sufficient money for his passage to America, in search of better prospects, it was a very emotional time for him and his sisters as they bid him farewell at the landing- stage at the Pier Head.

As soon as he settled down in America, he began to send his sisters money on a regular basis, he never sent his address for he was always on the move, hoping to obtain a regular job, because the recession was still going on, most of the employment was just cheap casual labour.

After a few years they never heard from their brother James, they couldn't trace his whereabouts, the last time they ever saw him in their lives was when they said farewell at the Pier Head.

The sisters decided they would have to enter into domestic service, it was a very hard decision to make but, they had no option, they had never been separated before, it was either that or to go begging on the streets, the last resort was the workhouse, before ending up in there, some took to stealing or prostitution quite a lot of young folks, male and female ended up committing suicide because they couldn't face going in to the workhouse, as the living conditions were absolutely filthy and appalling, degrading for human beings.

The sisters made a vow to each other that no matter what the circumstances were, they would always keep in contact with one another, it was a sad day for them, at least they would have a roof over their head, it was a bitter, freezing, icy damp and freezing winter with a strong, fierce gale force wind.

This true story reminds of the children's classic *Little Women*, by Louisa Alcott, except these four young girls had a much harder life to bear.

Margaret Ellen and Mary Ann both obtained posts as lady's maid, but they resided in different places, Mary Ann went to live in a large Victorian house in Woolton Village owned by a very wealthy lady.

She was delighted to hear that she would occupy a single bedroom all to herself, the food was excellent and her mistress treated her servants kindly.

In those days it was quite common for majority of young girls to be trained as milliners, she created fabulous hats for the gentry that they wore on special occasions she was thrilled when she discovered that Mary Ann was a professional milliner, she was extremely grateful for all the assistance she gave her in her spare time, she increased her salary, all the remnants and left over pieces of ribbons and lace and feathers and sequins she gave to Mary Ann, and she would adorn her Sunday hat, Mary Ann was happy in her new surroundings.

Margaret Ellen resided in a large Victorian house on Princess Boulevard, to be a ladies maid, you had to be very discreet, honest, cheerful, willing, intelligent and practically capable of turning your hands at needlework, hairdressing or whatever malady required of you.

The ladies maid had their own room with a cast iron single bed, a chest of drawers with a spotted design on the front of the drawers, a washstand, a water jug, a chamber pot, the servants had to wash in cold water even during the winter period it must have been unbearable.

The ladies maid were allowed far more privileges than the under class servants.

To summons for assistance from the servants downstairs, there was a set of bells and push buttons or cords in all the rooms used by the family, that indicated down to the basement to show what location needed the, there where no lifts in those Victorian houses, there where lots of flights of stairs starting from the cellar to the basement and to the very top of the attic.

The ladies maid had to be on call day and night to wait up if her mistress needs, if she had been up late attending a party or celebration, she would call her maid early hours in the morning to assist her with, her undressing, the poor maid would still have to be up bright and early the next day.

Catherine was also a ladies maid she resided in another large Victorian house In Childwall, her duties were exactly the same as the rest of the ladies -maid. They had to wear a uniform and buy it out of their own pocket, the dress material was serge, the colour was either dark brown, black, navy blue with black shoes and black lyle stockings with a small starched snow white apron.

On the front of their dress a starched small white cap or a long narrow silk ribbon pinned to the top of their head. They were not allowed to wear make- up or anything fancy, some of the mistresses often gave them their cast off clothes that had hardly been worn. The lower class servants quarters were exceedingly, poorly furnished, they had worn out paper thin towels, their bedroom consisted of just an old single cast-iron bed with a thin old lumpy flocked mattress, an old chest of drawers and a cast off chipped old water jug and a wash basin, if they were fortunate enough to have a mirror, which was very rare, it would be cracked, also they had to share a bedroom.

For church on Sunday mornings if their employer allowed them to attend, they had to wear long black coats and black shoes or black boots, a black maxi skirt with a white blouse, black gloves and a small black hat that was called a toque, it made them look old.

When my Mum was in her teens, for a short period she was employed as a kitchen maid, I only found this out recently while I was researching the family history. The kitchen maid came after the head kitchen maid; her duties were to assist the cook with all the preparations for the meals, etc.

If there was a big event going on she would receive some assistance from the scullery maid, after they had washed all the dishes and pans, they would go in to the scullery where there stood a large wooden sink then all the cutlery and the silver would be washed, dried and polished, the kitchens were situated downstairs where there was a large coal-fire grate with ovens on both sides of the fire for cooking, the heat from the ovens were controlled by the use of dampers, for the air draught to blaze through. Most houses used gas-mantles; there was no electricity during that period.

There was a large sink with a hot water tank, the passage leading to the larder was dank cool, with a stone flagged floor to the kitchen, coconut matting a large heavy wooden table, small wooden chairs, it was also used as a sitting room for the servants, it might have a draw at the side of the table for some of the maids to keep their personnel belongings in, for instance, needlework, books and such.

They had to be on call day and night to wait up for their mistress, if she had been up late party or some celebration, she would call her maid early hours in the morning to assist her with her undressing, the poor maid would still have to be up bright and early the next day.

Catherine was also a ladies maid she resided in a large Victorian house in Childwall, her duties were exactly the same as the rest of the ladies maids.

They had to wear a uniform and buy it out of their own pocket, the dress material was serge, the colour was either dark brown, navy blue or black, with black shoes and black lyle stockings and a small starched snow white apron on the front of their dress, and a starched small white cap or a long narrow silk ribbon pinned to the top of their head.

They were not allowed to wear make up or anything fancy, some of the mistresses often gave them their cast off clothes that had hardly been worn.

The lower class servants quarters were exceedingly, poorly furnished, they had worn out paper thin towels, their bedroom consisted of just an old single cast-iron bed with a thin lumpy flocked mattress, an old chest of drawers and a cast off chipped old water jug and a wash basin, if they were fortunate enough to have a mirror which was very rare, it would be cracked, they had to share a bedroom.

For church on Sunday mornings, if their employer allowed them to attend they had to wear long black coats and black shoes or boots with black stockings, a maxi black skirt with a white blouse, black gloves and a small black hat that was called a toque, it made them look quite older.

Catherine went to live in Childwall, she was employed as a parlour maid, her duties varied except, she had to rise at 6am then go downstairs to the drawing room and open up all the shutters, then go downstairs to the kitchen and take the breakfast tray upstairs to her mistress, while milady was bathing she would lay out her clothes and shoes and accessories, then return downstairs to check that the coal-fire had been lit, before her ladyship came downstairs. After that she would go in to the kitchen and have her own breakfast with the cook and housekeeper.

After having her breakfast she would tread softly again up all the flights of stairs in to the bedroom where her mistress would be patiently waiting for her to brush and comb and style her long tresses.

Downstairs again she would go, in to the drawing room and arrange all the flowers then, set the table for lunch, after lunch she would clear the table and lay it again for afternoon tea if no guests were calling on madam, madam would order her tea to be sent up stairs where she would be lounging on the settee in her bedroom.

Catherine would then water the plants in the drawing room then go downstairs to polish all the crystal glasses, after those chores were complete, her time was her own but, she was not allowed to go out in case her mistress required her assistance.

Bridget was employed as a TWEENY "The Model Maid " of all work; she resided in a large Victorian house in Aigburth road, not far from Otter spool.

Her work began at 5am every morning, her duties were practically everything, she would go downstairs to the kitchen in there was a vast coal-range fire where all the cooking was done, down on her hands and knees, she would rake out all the ashes from the fire, black lead the grate, the steel parts were burnished with emery paper.

She would scrunch up old newspapers into a small ball and place them in the fire grate, if there was wood and logs which was very seldom, they would be very damp and hard to light the fire, she would place some cinders on top of the paper balls and light it with a match, after it had begun to light she would gently add some pieces of coal on top and wait for the fire to get red for the kitchen maid to toast the bread. She would then clean out and light the fires in the drawing room and the dinning room.

All the fires in the house had to be lit in the autumn and wintertime, it wasn't too bad in the summer as there weren't many fires to light, but there was a lot of extra cleaning to be done while the family were on vacation.

Her next chore was to carry hot water in large burnished copper pots and stagger upstairs with them, besides carrying scuttles of coal upstairs also for the fires.

After TWEENY had attended to all those chores, she went downstairs again to the kitchen to assist the cook in preparing the meals, if she was lucky, and had a kind hearted cook she would invite her to come and sit at the long wooden table and offer her a cup cocoa and a thick slice of toast spread with dripping on it.

It was the same bored routine each day, scrubbing all the pots and pans, the kitchen table had to be scrubbed with fine sand, and the stone flagged kitchen floor had to be scrubbed she had attend to all the lowest menial tasks, such as scrubbing the front door steps, it was called flagging it was a horrible chore to do especially when the weather was freezing and icy and damp, wearing a long sack apron tied around her waist, with no warm clothes top protect her from the harsh weather, down on her hands and knees with a large bucket of hot water and a big piece of sandstone and a scrubbing brush and a thick string floor rag she would scrub, scrub, scrub her poor hands would be red raw, with all the rough work that she had to do.

She had to scrub lots of stone-flagged corridors, she would be completely exhausted when it came to her bedtime, she could just about manage to climb all the flights of stairs to the tiny attic bedroom, the bed was situated right by the stone wall no heating or ventilation, she would be that dead beat, sometimes it was too much of an effort to undress, she would just flop down on top of her bed and sink into a deep slumber dreaming of her knight in shinning armour, who would one day come along and suddenly sweep her off her feet and carry her away from her skiving job and take her away and marry so they would live happy ever after.

Some "TWEENY"S shared a tiny attic bedroom, there where no windows just a small skylight that had to be closed during the rainy season, they had no fresh air to breathe properly, the cast iron old worn out beds were so hard for them to sleep on, the springs of the bedstead stuck into their bodies the bedclothes were absolutely threadbare, they had no light except a tiny piece of candle stuck on to a cracked saucer, the piece of candle had to last for ages, and they were too scared to ask for another piece after that one had burnt out.

Their employers forbid them to read, especially the *Servants Magazine* for they didn't want them to be educated in fear of losing them to do their cheap labour.

The food the servants were served for Sunday breakfast was bloaters or sausages, a slice of bread and a cup of tea, for Sunday lunch they had the remainder of the family roast joint, a small serving of mashed potato, some vegetables and gravy.

For tea it was thin slices of bread and butter with jam, a small piece of home made cake or fruit pie and a cup of tea, the rest of the week they had left over from the family lunches and suppers.

Some of the poor servant girls were molested by their masters, while tier mistresses turned a blind eye to it, as soon as it became known that the poor young girl was pregnant her mistress would show no mercy, she would be instantly dismissed from her job and told to leave, immediately with no reference for her future, she would be cast out in to the streets, with no where else to go except the workhouse some of the most unfortunate would take to begging, stealing or prostitution, and before thinking of entering the wicked workhouse, they would commit suicide.

If the servants had a kind mistress she would allow them one day off each month from their duties, therefore Kate was quite fortunate as she was allowed it, this was a special day to her as she went to an afternoon tea-dance with her girl friend.

One lovely summer afternoon while she was at the dance suddenly, a handsome looking gentleman began to approach her, he politely asked her "If she would care to dance?"

She replied "That she would be delighted".

As they walked across the ballroom floor he opened out his arms Kate slowly melted in to them, they glided across the floor and began waltzing to a beautiful old fashion melody named "Music From The Great Gatsby" which came from the 1930s film *The Great Gatsby*. After the dance had ended he introduced himself to her saying that he was John MacEvoy then Kate told him that her name was Catherine O'Donnell,it was heavenly for her, while they were dancing time had stood still. She was falling in love with John suddenly, she awoke from her romantic dream she began to realise how fast the time had flown she would have to return to her drudging chores, while John accompanied her home he asked if he could see her again? Kate said that she would love to.

After their first date they began to see a lot more of each other. Then they started courting, during that period it was the custom of getting to know one another first, by asking your parents permission to invite your beau home to tea to see if they approved, in the front parlour there would be a great discussion with them concerning what race, religion and family background your beau came from.

The majority of people were against mixed races becoming sweethearts especially marrying, if they thought that your beau was suitable they would agree to you becoming engaged, then your sweetheart would take you down town to choose an engagement ring that is he was fortunate to be employed otherwise. You would have to make do with an imitation engagement ring from Woolworths stores until he could afford to buy you a proper ring. The engagement usually lasted about one year, or a few months more depending on their parents, they were quite old-fashion in their ways. Most of the courting was done in the front parlour if you happened to be out on a date you had to be home by 10pm otherwise the front door would be locked.

As soon John introduced Kate to his parents they took an instant

15

great liking to her, they invited her to stay for a special high tea in the front parlour after tea while his parents where in the kitchen John asked Kate if she would become engaged to him? She was thrilled and said yes she would be so happy to.

On her next day off from work he took her down town to select an engagement ring then they went and had afternoon tea in apish café to celebrate their engagement then he escorted her back home to her lodgings.

Kate went straight upstairs to her attic room which she shared with another maid, who was still on duty she took her engagement ring out of the sky blue velvet padded box and put it on a fine piece of cord then, she placed it around her neck and tied it in a secure knot and tucked it inside of her bosom so that nobody could see it because, if their employers found out that they had become engaged they would be immediately dismissed as they didn't want to lose them, they would be put out in to the streets without a reference to seek employment elsewhere they would end up starving and become destitute.

Twelve months later John proposed to Kate, she accepted with sheer joy. so they set a date for their wedding, she decided that she would love to be a June bride the sad part of it was she couldn't share her happiness with her servant friends in case it reached the ears of her mistress she was astonished because just before she was about to leave her employment she told her mistress the glad tidings when her mistress heard about Kate getting married she told her that she was very happy for her although she would be sincerely sorry to lose her as she had been such a loving devoted servant. She gave Kate her blessings and a wonderful reference for a wedding present she presented her with a beautiful black leather bound gold leaf paged holy bible.

Kate went to live with John's parents until they were later

married I heard that their wedding was a grand affair.

A year later Kate gave birth to a lovely baby girl who was christened Mary a few months after they moved in to their new home
a two-roomed terraced house that was built inside of a court it
was called Crawshaw Court I believe that majority of the folks
who lived there were Irish or Irish decent there where a few more
courts but Crawshaw Court was the main one.

As you entered the court it had small-boxed houses on either side
in the centre of the court was a cold water tap at the top end of the
court there where two outside toilets one on each side, there
where stables one of the lads kept his donkey their some of the
men kept their shire horses in the stables, I can always remember
the smell of hay and straw.

During that period there weren't criminals about most folks used
to tie their front door key on a piece of thick string leaving it
hanging inside the letter box all you had to do was put your hand
through the letter box and pull out the key to let yourself in every-
body trusted one another with the exception of a few rascals. Poor
folks didn't have any valuables to be stolen the few that have had
were already pawned.

A year after Kate conceived again this time she gave birth to a
bouncing baby boy with a mop of red hair sea blue eyes he was
baptised Patrick after his grandfather Patrick O'Donnell.

When Patrick grew up although he never attended college he was
exceedingly clever he was as good as any lawyer he would solve
all his friends and neighbour and relatives personnel problems
for them there was no legal aid then.

Mary Patrick's sister married John Turner they raised a family,
there was Johnny Kathleen Monica and Terry they were quite

well off compared to most of our neighbours aunt Mary was me Dad's cousin she was my favourite aunt she was a lovely jolly lady and was me Mums best friend she run a provident club for all the neighbours during that period people were far much poorer but much more caring towards each other.

Aunt Mary and uncle John always took us to see a pantomime every Christmas at the Pavilion in Lodge Lane I remember one year going to see the pantomime walking along the street with Johnny my second cousin he was walking a head of me I noticed a chewing gum machine stuck on the wall if you inserted a half-penny in the slot machine a packet of P K .spearmint came out of the bottom of the machine and for every forth coin the went in you got two packets of spearmint, I happened to bang on the machine as I was passing by well I never, for who ever ad been attending to it they had forgotten to lock it out came packets and packets of spearmint I had a jersey on I held it open to catch them all I was calling Johnny to come and help me I was so excited I can't remember any more of that lovely incident.

Margaret Ellen, Mary Ann and Bridget were still in domestic service but in different places, they arranged to have the same day off so that they could go and visit their sister Kate and her family.

During the winter time, they would gather around the coal-fire in Kate's front parlour reminisce their childhood memories and their dear departed brother in America if the weather was grand they would take the children to Sefton Park to feed the ducks and swans later they would have a lovely picnic.

The servants were rarely seen except on special occasions at Christmas-time they would all assemble in the main hall to receive their Christmas present their mistress or master would call out their names starting from the highest ranks when they had been presented with their present they would wish each other "A Merry Christmas" the servant would thank their employer the female servants would do a small curtsy then go back in line until they had all received their Christmas present.

If they had a kind employer after they had attended to all the guests, the guests would go in to the ballroom where they would dance the night away until the early hours of the morning the servants would then return to their quarters to enjoy their own Christmas merriment.

On Margaret Ellen's day off from her duties usually first she would go to St Patrick's church in Park Place in Liverpool and have a talk with the parish priest, one day while she was there a young American chap arrived to see the priest the priest introduced them to one another after a short while, his housekeeper came and interrupted them telling him that he was wanted on the phone immediately as it was very urgent he then excused his self while he was absent Frederick asked Margaret Ellen if he could see her again before he returned to America ?Margaret Ellen said that she would love to.

After a few months Frederick returned to Liverpool they were getting along quite well and they began seeing more of each other, then he went back to America, later on his arrival back to Liverpool he asked Margaret Ellen if she would become engaged to him she said that she would be happy to so he took her down town to choose her engagement ring, the sad thing was that she had to do exactly the same thing as Kate, which was to hide it inside her bosom.

Frederick returned back to America for a few months on business, on his return he proposed to Margaret Ellen she accepted his proposal she was very much in love with him, later they were married in St Patrick's church in the district called Gerry Hill.

Margaret Ellen was thrilled at first then, she experienced a deep sad feeling at the thought of leaving her loving sisters behind fortunately for her the ship had not sailed when she discovered that she had married a bigamist, it was the ships porter who had enlightened her as he had assisted her on board with her luggage he told her, that Frederick was a very wealthy man who frequently came to Liverpool on business and that he was already married with a wife and a son.

Poor Margaret Ellen she was utterly speechless, she couldn't believe all this was happening to her she went in to the cabin frantically searching through Frederick's belongings suddenly she came across a photograph of him and his lawful wedded wife with their son posing in the centre she was absolutely dumbstruck, now she knew for certain it was true and not just a nightmare.

As quick as lightening she made her way in a horse and cab straight to her sister Kate.

As Kate heard the carriage draw up outside her front door she drew back the lace curtain in the front parlour as she glanced through the window to her amazement she saw Margaret Ellen stagger out of the carriage approaching her front door as Kate rushed out Margaret Ellen was just about to collapse Kate gently took hold of her are and guided her inside to the front parlour after she had tried her best to calm her down, she went in to the kitchen to make a cup of tea after giving her the tea she asked her why she was in such an emotional state Margaret Ellen tried to compose herself before she told her the tragic news Kate was flabbergasted she couldn't believe what she was hearing.

When Frederick realised that Margaret Ellen had vanished he became furious he was in such terrible rag, brandishing a revolver he headed straight for Kate's home.

When he eventually arrived there he began hammering on her front door and shouting threatening to kill Margaret Ellen suddenly, Kate's husband appeared on the scene John was a very strong man first, he tried to restrain him until the police arrived then they escorted him in to the police wagon and took him to the bridal for further questioning.

Margaret Ellen didn't press any charges against him so he was warned against his violent behaviour, and then taken back to the ship. Margaret Ellen was a devout Catholic during that period the Catholic Church didn't approve of divorce, it was unheard of in their religion. She was never the same after that shocking episode a few months later she was admitted to the Women's hospital in Shaw Street where she underwent a major operation after the operation she contacted pneumonia also she lost the will to live, she suffered a broken heart and passed away in hospital.

Me Dad loved Margaret Ellen she was his favourite auntie and a rare fine lady he always said she was a shrine, he was so proud of her she attended his wedding but she only stayed for a brief period.

On Mary Ann's day off duty one lovely autumn afternoon as she was strolling by the lake in Sefton Park the skies were pale blue mixed with small white patches that looked like fleecy lambs wool the swans and ducks were floating in the water you could hear the cries of delight as children cast pieces of bread in to the lake for the animals.

The leaves on the trees had turned from grass green to russet and gold some leaves came twirling down fro the branches with the gentle breeze the birds were chirping merrily away, the crythamums were in full bloom.

As she went and sat down upon a bench a handsome looking

gentleman sat down beside her, he asked her if she would object to him sitting there? She said that she did not mind, he then introduced himself to her, his name was George Crozier. After a while he asked he if she would give him the pleasure of seeing her again? She paused awhile and then replied that she would love to.

The next time they met they went out strolling then they continued seeing one another for a few months ten George opened up his heart and confessed to her that he was falling deeply, in love with her Mary Ann said that she felt the same way about him so they decided to become engaged she had to do exactly the same as her sisters had done when they became engaged that was to hide her engagement ring deep down inside her bosom.

Twelve months later they set a date for their wedding they agreed to wait for a year to give them time to save up sufficient money for their new home. The good news was that a week before the wedding Mary Ann told her mistress that she would be leaving and the reason why, as her mistress was a very caring lady instead of instantly dismissing her she gave her blessings and even helped her to create her own wedding dress and a beautiful head-dress the colour was ashes of roses with matching accessories.

After their wedding they went to live with George's parents until they could obtain a house of their own they soon succeeded a few months later they rented a small terraced house.

When they settled down in their new home they were so happy then as time went by Mary Ann became pregnant she had a beautiful baby girl who was christened Susan then later on she gave birth to Mary then after Mary Margaret was born then Dolly was born and last of all a son James.

Their father was a protestant and a firm believer in rights and wrongs their mother was catholic but she had to have her children brought up as protestants she passed away quite young Dolly was just a little girl then, when the girls grew up they all married except Dolly and James he went out to work so did Dolly she also took care of her Dad and her brother.

I was very fond of Uncle George he had a lovely sense of humour he smoked a pipe I loved the aroma of the tobacco sometimes I would go on errands for him one Saturday afternoon he gave me some money to go on a message as I was happily skipping along with the florin in my hand it slipped out of my hand and went down a grid in the street I went back looking all forlorn when I told him what had happened he just started laughing he always saw the funny side of things.

I loved going over to Dolly's I was just a little girl Dolly looked like a film star in the Roaring Twenties she really knew how to dress and make up, she was courting a lovely chap named Jimmy Tasker they made a lovely couple he used to come to her home to court her, he always brought her a box of expensive chocolates for her and a small bottle of whiskey for uncle George.

Madge Law and I used to be fascinated watching Dolly make up her face, you know when you're a little girl well we would try to imitate her, once we shaved our eyebrows we made a real mess we looked a terrible sight, after they became engaged they set a date for their wedding sadly to say I wasn't there I was away at that time and couldn't attend.

They had a lovely family, uncle George passed away Dolly and James raised a family there's Jean George James and Louise on Dolly's side of the family Susan Mary and James and Maggie have all passed away Peggy who is Susan's daughter lives next door to Dolly it was so nostalgic for me to see them all after so many years Dolly is my Dad's first cousin they were all a very close and happy family.

Bridget washed herself in cold water then she began her daily duties that included cleaning out all the fires and the kitchen ranges carrying large buckets of coal lightening all the fires and the kitchen ranges then carry bowls of hot water upstairs for the family to have their morning wash scrub out all the pots and pans then scrub the long wooden kitchen table by sprinkling it with fine sand then rinsing it of in cold water lots of flagged floors and long flagged corridors had to be scrubbed also.

After breakfast she would take up all the mats carry them in to the back yard and give them a good beating the best carpets had to be sprinkled with damp used tea leaves and left on for a few minutes then, down on her hands and knees she would brush them all off there where lots of bric-a-brac to be polished and cleaned.

TWEENY had to attend to the lowest menial tasks such as scrubbing all the stone flags and the front door step using a large piece of sandstone to scrub the steps it was a tedious chore down on her hands and knees her poor hands were red raw with all the scrubbing especially with no warm clothes to protect her from the bitter icy wind and sleet and snow and rain, she had to polish all the families boots and shoes, empty the chamber pots clean out the toilets her life was sheer drudgery.

George Jones was born in a small beautiful village in South Wales called Tonypandy his parents were Presbyterians his father was a coal-miner and he sang in the Welsh male choir George followed in his fathers footsteps he sang in the choir when he became a young man he had a baritone voice just like his father.

During that period there was a depression going on so George decided to seek employment elsewhere he started off walking to Liverpool resting at various places and sleeping on farms where he was given food and shelter in return for doing manual work for the farmers he was a pleasant sort of chap the gentleman type he always wore a buttonhole with a flower and foliage on the lapel of his jacket eventually he arrived in Liverpool where he was fortunate to obtain casual work and a decent lodging he soon began to settle down.

On a beautiful spring day one Sunday afternoon while he was out strolling through Sefton Park the robin redbreast hopping merrily upon the grass while the birds were chirping to one another, the buds of the blossom trees were gradually coming in bloom in various shades of petal pink ,lilac and snow white and the daffodils and crocuses and tulips were beginning to bloom through to a new spring George happened to glance up and behold a beautiful elegant pretty young lady was passing by he raised his cap to greet her good afternoon shyly she looked up with her sky blue eyes and gave him a demur smile she reminded him of the picture of "The Mona Lisa" he walked slowly towards her raised his cap again then he introduced himself to her telling her his name and where he originally came from, the young lady then introduced herself to him her name was Bridget O' Donnell there was a lovers seat nearby where they went and sat down during the conversation Bridget told George that she was employed in domestic service as a TWEENY, for a while they just sat there listening to the birds chirping away and feeling the gentle breeze blowing by and the grass fluttering with the breeze, the perfume from the flowers was heavenly to poor Bridget after being closed in scivvying away all those long hours with no fresh air.

George wished to see Bridget again so he asked her if she would like to see him again? She said she would be delighted to they both agreed to meet on the love seat where they had first met from the first moment he saw her he had fell completely in love with her Bridget felt the same way about him too, he didn't waste any time for the next time that they met he proposed to her and she accepted she was over the moon with happiness they arranged to be married very soon they didn't want a long engagement they were married in St Patrick's church in the district called Gerry Hill.

After their wedding they went to live at No 2. Back Myrtle street where their first child George was born a few months later they moved to 19. Bancroft street to a small four bedroom house it was near the Abatar back of Parliament Fields there where stables at the back of the court with small boxed houses on each side with a cold water tap in the centre of the court, they were fortunate to have an inside toilet in their house and not situated in the back yard like the rest of their neighbours the only problem was there was no bathroom in the houses they all had to use the public baths and the public washhouse to wash their clothes majority of the families who couldn't afford the cost of the public baths would heat the water on the fire and pour it in to a aluminium bath and the family got bathed in front of the coal fire in the kitchen.

3
DABBER

Uncle Jim was me Dads' only brother he was very special to us he was loved by all the children in our neighbourhood he was a happy go lucky person kind and considerate to everyone we were not allowed to call him Dabber that was his nick name by every one else.

When he was working on the docks as a casual labourer assisting to unload the cargo boats when he was working on the banana boats he would always bring home two large bunches of green bananas and give them to me Mum she would put them in the airing cupboard until they were ripe enough for us to eat give the other bunch she would give to her neighbours each in turn fruit was a rare luxury in those days and also quite expensive people were living on the breadline there was a depression still going on.

When Uncle Jim was unemployed he would stand outside Martindale's coal yard with the rest of the men and young lads who were all in the same predicament they would form a long que and wait anxiously listening for their names to be called out for a casual job without any references or cards if they were fortunate enough to be called out they would have to weigh up one-hundred weight of coal and slack and shovel it in to a coal sack and lift it on to the coal wagon the job might last for a day or just a few hours it all depended on the order all this was done in   all kinds of foul weather just for a few measly shillings but it meant a great deal to them financially and it also boosted their confidence knowing that they weren't idle they would hand around Martindale's coal yard every day except Sunday seeking work.

When the children were coming out of school some of them had to cross over Crown street which was a very dangerous road it was right opposite Martindale's if Uncle Jim happened to be there he would see them all safely across the road just like a traffic warden'. After Uncle Jims' Mother Gran O' Donnell passed away he came to live in our house for a while but him and Mum didn't see eye to eye but she always cared for him.

One winters day he decided to go for a stroll a short while later a thick dense fog began to appear suddenly the fog horns started blowing one hour later he hadn't returned we all began to cry as we thought that he had got lost in the fog eventually he arrived home we were so happy to see him safe we were hugging him so joyfully.

He suffered severely with rheumatism in his hands and feet it was caused through the (1914) war when he was in the army in the trenches and with working out in the foul weather he never complained. After a while he left our house and went to board at Mrs Clegg's in Mona street it wasn't far from where we lived the day he left we were all crying we didn't want him to leave but he promised us faithfully he would always come and visit us and that we could go and visit him anytime we wanted to, he kept his solemn promise our house didn't seem the same after he had gone we missed him more than words could ever say.

Sometimes Uncle Jim got his shopping on tick, he would pay his bill weekend my young sister Mary loved going for his errands she would feel quite grown up with a straw basket on her arm and the shopping list in her hand the list would include twenty woodbines cigarette tobacco rizla papers matches groceries and toiletries.

One day he asked Mary to go on an errand she was delighted to go off she went when she arrived at the shop she gave the shopping list to the shop keeper the shop keeper asked Mary if she would kindly tell him that he hadn't paid his last bill Mary returned home and delivered the message to him he was flabbergasted because he thought that he had paid the bill, he was a very honest person probably he must have had a few drinks too many and his memory had slipped'. Immediately he wrote an apology note and enclosed the cash with a new order when the shop keeper read the note she smiled and said to Mary that she understood his mistake she put all the items in Mary's basket later on me Mum got to hear of the shopping event she told Mary not to go on any more errands for him Mary still went for them.

Some of our family called Uncle Jim Gaga my young departed brother Tony, his grand children used to call him Gaga also and Tony always kept the same tradition as Uncle Jim on New Year's Eve dressing up and gathering all the families together.

I recall one New Year's Eve when I was a little girl Uncle Jim and his pal dressed up as women for a laugh they played the part so well wearing silk stockings and high heeled shoes a long evening dress with all the accessories and an imitation shoulder fur fox and a handbag on their arm, they made such a grand entrance in to their local pub all the neighbours started staring at them wondering who were these strangers were and where they came from suddenly Big Ben began to strike on the midnight hour the New Year was coming in every one was wishing one another Happy New Year all at once the two men threw off their wigs and revealed themselves the applause was tremendous, they were the talk of the district it had always been the custom to dress up for the New Year.

Uncle Jim was quite musical it ran in their family he couldn't half play the harmonica he would cover it with an empty glass to give it a better sound he used to play the spoons also sometimes he would get two flat bones from the butcher's then smooth them down and show us how to play music then he showed us how to get a comb put a piece of tissue paper over it and play some sounds.

Every Sunday after having his breakfast he would take a stroll to the Pier Head from there he would walk to Windsor street to visit my elder sister Frances and her family it was a ritual to him no matter what the weather was like he never missed going to see them he loved her children he used to take toys for them they weren't new but it was the act of love that counted after having his roast dinner with them Frances or I would make a pot of tea uncle Jim would sit by the fire reading the News' of the World then he would do the crosswords he was brilliant at that, when he had completed the crosswords we would all gather around the fire listening to him telling the children lovely stories he was a good story teller. When he was ready to go home Frances always gave him books and candles we always gave him cigarettes and tobacco and rizla papers and candles so he could read in his bed-room, he had a small cigarette machine and a small tin box that he kept his tobacco in he was a real bookworm he loved browsing in the book shops and going to the public libraries he wore steel rimmed spectacles on the rim of them he had a piece of sticking plaster to prevent them from slipping down.

One winters night there was a fierce gale blowing the wind was screeching and howling down the chimney slates were falling off the roof tops Margaret said to her brother John oh poor Uncle Jim he cant' go home in this terrible gale John said he can stay here with us in our house.

My nephew Tommy told me that he always remembers when he was a boy Uncle Jim gave him oranges we all loved him so much he was our special favourite uncle when he passed away we were terribly sad even although he is gone he will never be forgotten by me.

4
THE DEPRESSION (1930s)

When Margaret Wilkinson was a young girl she trained to be a milliner after that she entered in to domestic service and was employed as a kitchen maid when the maids went in to domestic service they had to take three print dresses, a blue apron, a white bibbed apron and a thick course hessian apron, they wore a black alpaca dress that reached down to their ankles the rules were that their legs must never be seen.

For afternoon wear they wore white large muslin aprons with frills attached to the bands that reached over their shoulders, they wore black shoes and black lyle stockings they had to buy their uniform out of their own pocket, it had to starched and spotless.

The kitchen maid had a tiny attic room it had no windows just a small skylight which had to be close in the winter time and the rainy season, her cast-iron bed had a worn out lumpy mattress, threadbare blankets and paper thin worn out bed sheets, a cast off chest of drawers, a chipped wash basin, a water jug and a wash stand, no carpet or linoleum just bare floorboards, no light except a tiny piece of candle stuck to an old saucer. She had to assist the cook in every way possible and help to prepare the vegetables and all the meals.

I cant' recall when Margaret my Mum met George one evening she told me when I asked her how she me Dad she told me that, she was out walking with her girlfriend, she was wearing high-

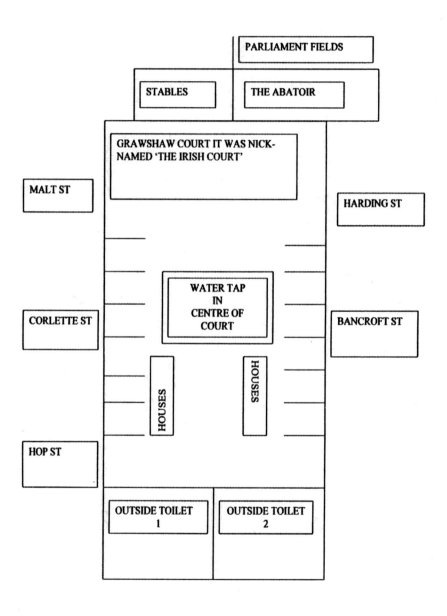

PARLIAMENT FIELDS

STABLES

THE ABATOIR

GRAWSHAW COURT IT WAS NICK-
NAMED 'THE IRISH COURT'

MALT ST

HARDING ST

WATER TAP
IN
CENTRE OF
COURT

CORLETTE ST

BANCROFT ST

HOUSES

HOUSES

HOP ST

OUTSIDE TOILET
1

OUTSIDE TOILET
2

Bancroft Street

Harding Street 1934

heel shoes suddenly one of the heels came loose she stopped to try and fix it a chap passing by seeing the predicament she was in came to her rescue he introduced himself to her his name was George Jones then Margaret introduced herself and her girlfriend he made a date with Margaret after which they started courting.

They were married in a few months time and went and rented a furnished flat in Mrs Dubbers house in Mona street Margaret became pregnant she had a beautiful baby girl who was christened Margaret then the next child she had was a lovely baby girl who was baptised Frances named after Mums' sister, they were such a happy family until the year (1922) on New Years Eve Dad had not long gone out to meet his pals to celebrate the New Year coming in Frances was asleep in her cot in the living room Margaret was playing with her doll that Santa Claus had brought her there was a strong steel fire-guard with a brass rod on top surrounding the coal-fire which was lit Mum had just finished washing some clothes she went downstairs to the cellar to hang up the clothes to dry, as she was ascending back upstairs suddenly she got such an unbearable pain she sat down for a few minutes waiting for the pain to ease off she got up and slowly walked upstairs to the living room she was about to open the door when a great gush of fierce flames came rushing out towards her she let our such an unmerciful scream one of the lodgers nick named Butcher who worked in a butchers shop came dashing out of his room as he heard the screams he grabbed hold of little Margaret wrapped her up n an old piece of carpet and tried to smoother out the flames she was severely burnt, Mum fought her way through the flames to rescue little Frances Mrs Dubber took hold of Frances the ambulance arrived immediately and they were all taken to the hospital Margaret was admitted she was treated for shock and server burns and puemonia a few hours later she passed away Frances was taken to Aunt Tottie Mums' eldest sister a few hours after Mum gave birth to a baby boy later he was christened George after me Dad poor Dad he was speechless when he heard the shocking news he couldn't take it in and poor Mum she suffered a severe breakdown she didn't even know that Maggie had passed away her sister Tottie buried Maggie.

Frances and Georgie stayed with aunt Tottie for a while then it was decided that they should go into an orphanage until Mum recovered the day they left for the orphanage it was a bitter cold day when they arrived there Matron greeted them and took them from their Dad he was broken hearted at leaving them there he had no choice in the hall there was a blazing coal-fire. Frances took Georgie by the hand towards the fire to get warm she was like a little Mother to him they were perished from the bitter icy wind. She told me that she can always picture the children's the window waving them goodbye, off they went on their homeward journey.

Frances and Georgie didn't know what was happening to their poor Mother, when they arrived home there she was waiting for them with open arms Dad did his utmost to comfort Mum, telling her that she was recovering she was still in deep shock I know that she never got over it, she often spoke of Maggie she kept a photograph of her from when she was about two or three years of age posing although she looked as if she was sulking to me as if she didn't want to have her picture taken.

Mum became pregnant again she gave birth to a fine baby born he was christened Gerard after he was born Mum conceived again and had a lovely baby girl who was baptised Bridget, after Gran O' Donnell then along came another baby boy he was baptised Thomas after Mum's brother.

Frances was named after Mum's sister I don't know who Gerry was named after later on mum gave birth to another baby girl she was christened Mary after me Dad's cousin, then she conceived again baby boy named James after me Dad's brother, then Tony was born and then Vera after Vera came John and last of all Billy was born sad to say poor Billy passed away when he was just a baby.

The only way the poor working class folks could survive was run by a government scheme called "The Poor Mans Relief" it meant that an inspector would call around unexpectedly to see if you was doing any kind of work one of the neighbours was always on the look out he would pass the word around so they would be on their guard so they could hide anything of value that they had unfortunately if they hadn't time to hide the articles as he came to make his unexpected visit his eyes would roam all around if he spotted anything of value spotted him coming when the inspector entered the house his eyes would roam all around to see if they had any valuables that you could sell or he would tell them to pawn. He would begin his enquiries which was called the mean's test if they passed the test he would give them a voucher they would take it to the grocers shop hand it in to the grocer in return they would receive a small quantity of food if the hadn't passed the means test they would have to pawn what ever they possessed clocks, radio new boots shoes or jewellery clothes.

The men and the young lads did gardening and decorating and various jobs for the gentry, during the harsh winters when the snow lay deep upon the ground they all went snow shifting clearing all the piles of snow from the drives, gardens some of the kind owners from the estates and posh houses left orders with a servant to invite them in to the servants quarters after they had completed their work in the kitchen they would be given a hot cuppa cocoa and a sandwich, then they would be paid for their work.

The lads used to go around to all of the fruit shops asking for empty wooden boxes which they would take home and help their dad in the back yard to chop them up in to small bundles of firewood, tie them up with string or elastic bands or with a small piece of wire they would go around the streets selling them.

Monday mornings a lot of us would be absent from school we would have to go to the pawn shop named Speakmans in Crown street usually it would be me dads' best suit or his best pair of shoes he never knew about it as it was done in secret, Mum used to say don't' let your father know about it she would get it out on Friday or Saturday morning he would be none of the wiser I think he had an idea what was going on he never mentioned the matter as he knew how hard it was for me Mum to make ends meet when some of the men discovered their suits or shoes had gone missing the wives got a good hiding as it prevented them from going out to the pub If the women didn't have anything left to pawn they would make up a clothes bundle me Mum would select the best clothes that she could find wash them and hang them on the fire- guard to dry then she would iron them and neatly fold them make up a bundle then wrap them in a nice clean pinafore she would tell me how much to ask for the pawn broker wasn't supposed to serve us if he was in a good mood he would if not one of our neighbours would pledge it for us she would ask us how much we wanted he would always knock us down you seldom got what you asked for we could hear the women bantering with him over the amount they needed, the neighbour would give us the cash and the pawn ticket to give to our Mother.

The last straw for the poor women if they had nothing else left to pawn was their wedding ring this caused them to lose their dignity some of them would tie a band around their wedding finger or an imitation wedding from Woolworths that's' if they could afford to buy one if the pledge had lost its value he wouldn't accept it in a loud harsh voice he would shout out the reason the poor women felt humiliated if he changed his mind after a lot of persuasion and accepted their pledge relief would spread all over their face the shop was always packed you had to queue up and wait ages to be served but they weren't proud they had their families to care for.

He would inspect every article to see if they were worn out or torn if they were not up to his standard he would shout out to them and say Mrs so +so I am not taking in any more perishable goods only gold rings, gold sovereigns and watches he was a walking goldmine. Sometimes if the articles were new and the women were anxious for more money which they always were he would buy the goods from them they always lost out on the deal he knew how to bargain with them it was his profession they had no choice it was either that or starve.

Our teacher always knew the reason why most of us were absent on a Monday morning as we had to go to the pop-shop we used to sing a rhyme about it, it goes like this.

> Old Mary Ellen at the pawnshop door
> With a bundle in her hand and a bundle on the floor
> She asked for 4/ 6d.
> And he only gave he 4/ -
> So she knocked the bloody knocker off the pawnshop door

Some of the women who had a few coppers to spare did washing for the gentry the clothes had to be soaked first in cold water then washed boiled and rinsed the white clothes had to be steeped in cold water washed then rinsed and soaked again in cold water with a reckitts blue block and rinsed again then starched last of all they were ironed with an old cast iron which was heated on the coal-fire when it was red or heated on the range they had no modern appliances all this was done by hand they would wring out the clothes with their bare hands or with an old cast iron clothes mangle.

Some of the women who had a few pence extra took the gentries washing to the public washhouse they had to keep their eyes wide open in case the washing got stolen by some rouges who would sell it or pawn it.

The women who went house cleaning had to work very hard just to earn a few coppers they never complained they were grateful for small mercies as long as they had sufficient food and shelter for their families.

Me Mum saved our worn out shoes and she would repair them herself she would buy a piece of shoe leather some rivets and a thatching end in cast they needed a stitch she had a small shoe flask a small sharp knife and a small hammer I used to be fascinated watching her mending our shoes she would measure the worn out part and chalk it soak the patch of leather place it on the shoe or boot nail it down and smooth it around the sole or heel with the knife and colour it to match she did the job just as good as the cobbler it was much cheaper for her.

When I brought my school friends home with me if it was raining or snowing first thing she would say to us was take off those wet clothes and shoes and socks she would give us a clean dry towel ourselves then she would give us nice dry old clean clothes to wear after that she would make us a lovely hot cuppa cocoa and a thick jam butty.

Me Dad was tall slim and debonair looking with his deep set blue eyes jet black hair and his open neck shirt wearing a cravat loosely tied around his neck and a nice waistcoat and trousers and black leather shoes he had a real gipsy look about him he was loving and peaceful to be with he never raised his voice to us if we were being argumentative he would say "Keep the peace" if we were feeling a bit down he always said to us "Come on best foot forward".

When he was a young boy living in the orphanage with his brother James he learnt to play the bugle he was brilliant at it they nick named him the bugle boy he was a marvellous born dancer from tap and step dance to military dancing he could do any dance.

We all loved Saturday nights the grown ups would have a hole-ly after the pubs closed Uncle John and Aunt Mary and some of me Dads' friends and our relatives would come to our house there would be such merriment dancing singing each of them doing a turn we would sit on the stairs having the time of our lives dads' favourite song was "Strolling" Mums' favourite was "Three O Clock In The Morning" they didn't have any musical instruments but they still had a good old sing song a man would play the spoons another would play the harmonica in some homes they had a piano or a piano accordion my cousin Girlie Wilkinson could play the piano accordion beautiful my eldest sister Frances is a marvellous piano player on Saturday nights in Myrtle Gardens she would play in Mrs Graham s house for them.

Me dad was the best dad in the world to us born a gentleman died a gentleman on his resting place I've had engraved.

> *When the breeze gently blows*
> *A beautiful memory.*
> *This song id dedicated to him.*
> *Strolling just strolling by the light of the moon above'*
> *I don't' envy the rich in their automobile*
> *For a motorcar is phoney Id' sooner have shanks and ponies*
> *When I'm strolling just strolling*
> *By the light of the moon above*
> *Every night I go out strolling for I know my luck is rolling*
> *When I'm strolling with the one I love.*

The women had to queue up for hours on end outside the fruit shops in the snow it would be about six inches deep sometimes just to buy potatoes they were very scarce at that time the worst part of it was when it came to their turn sometimes there would be none left.

The men queued up outside Martindales coal-yard in Crown Street to buy a quarter of a hundred weight of coal it was all they could afford and all that they were allowed only just sufficient to keep a small fire going and the winters were very server we would search through all the cupboards looking for old worn out shoes and boots pieces of old linoleum pieces of cardboard anything to keep the fire burning potato peelings vegetable peelings then we would rake out all the cinders from underneath the fire put them on top and add wet tea leaves to bank it.

Some of the children roamed around Lime St station as the trains departed and arrived they would run up to the gentry travellers saying to them "Carry your bag Sir or Madam" Some of them would just nod or murmur yes they would walk along beside them carrying their luggage until the passenger ascended the train or got in to a cab they would give them a few coppers some of the little vagabonds would hop it with the luggage it reminds me of Fagan the travellers began to get wise to their tricks they weren't all rouges in the evenings just before five o clock you could hear the cries of the paper lad shouting Echo Exi Echo he would run all around the streets in the district selling his Echo.
Majority of the women especially the Mary Ellen's' wore men's caps wrapped around their shoulders they wore woollen shawls, no matter how destitute they were most of them possessed a good coat that they saved for special occasions those who were too unfortunate to have one would always borrow one from their neighbour or friend or relative, they always shared and helped each other.

The men were in the same predicament they had to do the same borrowing suits and ties and hats times were very hard for them they were all living far below the breadline.

A lot of the poor children attended the dinner house during their school days I cant' recall if they attended during the school holidays it was for their midday meal which was the only meal they had for the whole day except a jam butty and a cuppa cocoa for their tea when they arrived home.

We didn't attend the dinner house once I went with my girlfriend I sneaked in unknown to me Mum that day they had mince meat mashed potatoes vegetables and gravy for seconds we had suet pudding and custard tasted nice but I didn't enjoy the dinner'.

No matter what the circumstances were of these poor unfortunate folks they had a great sense of humour it prevented them from breaking down it helped them to survive the poverty and destitution, when the rag and bone came around shouting "Any old rags" one of the neighbours would shout out "here comes the rag man pull yourself together" I often heard a whisper that some poor man or woman had committed suicide as they couldn't bear the condition of life any longer'.

I remember vividly when I was a little girl we lived in a court in Bancroft Street near the Abatar Parliament Fields there was a cast iron tap in the middle of the court where we used to go to draw water one lovely summers day as I was out playing with my friends suddenly we heard such a commotion we stopped playing and looked up to see what was happening we saw some of the women from the court carrying wooden rolling pins chasing a man he was running for all his might it was like "Chariots of Fire" he scampered as fast as his legs could take him getting no rent from them it was the rent collector all the children and onlookers were hysterical with laughter.

The folks had to economise a great deal nothing was ever thrown out what ever food was placed in front of you at meal times you had to eat it you had no choice if you didn't like it you just made do with a jam butty.

A lot of the young lasses went step-flagging scrubbing the door steps for the gentry in all kinds of weather and polishing the brass door knockers just for a few measly coppers. I remember one incident a few of us went step-flagging it was a bitterly cold day we went to a large Victorian house on Princess Boulevard unknown to our parents of course, one of the girls was wearing real old worn out shoes with a hole on the sole and apiece of cardboard inside to keep out the cold as we were cleaning inside the house one of the girls saw a pair of ladies shoes she told our friend to try them on lucky for her they fitted her as her friend was just about to throw them out of the window so they would fall on the grass and we could collect them on our way out, unfortunately the plan back fired we were caught red handed the owner of the house saw the shoes flying out of the window looking very annoyed she summoned us altogether and asked us who the culprit was no one uttered a word with our heads handing down in shame nobody would confess, we were all terrified that she was going to call the police after a while she noticed the lass with the worn out shoes she called her to one side and told one of us to go down in to the garden and bring up her shoes the lass obeyed fetched up the shoes the lady told the girl to try them on they fitted her nicely she was told to keep them and discard of her old worn out ones she shyly thanked the lady the lady asked us all to promise her sincerely that we would never do such a foolish thing again we all promised that we wouldn't shoes or no shoes.

I always loved dancing when I was a little girl Mum always scolded me for wearing out my shoes by dancing we would take our shoes to the cobblers and get him to put steel toe and heel caps on them so we could tap-dance we couldn't afford red tap-shoes Mum used to say if I catch you don't' stop dancing you will be wearing police-clogs that would petrify me then as soon as she went indoors I would start dancing again before I went indoors I would give my shoes a little polish with a piece of rag some of us were dance mad we even use to skip and we made up this rhyme

Dancing Dolly she had no sense
Bought some eggs for eighteen pence
The eggs were bad Dolly went mad
Pitch patch pepper

My cousin Nellie and I where in the same class one year her family were well off financially I remember onetime she had a lovely summer dress lemon organdie with a flower pattern it was handed down to me I had to wear it for school one day one of the girls in our class started making fun of me calling out that I was wearing Nellie's dress I felt humiliated I went home crying when Mum saw me she asked me what was wrong I told her about the incident in the classroom she immediately told me to go and take the dress off I couldn't take it off fast enough'

Another incident I recall was when one of our neighbours gave Mum a black maxi coat she altered it to fit me it had a cross over collar with two lapels that fastened with two long shaped buttons I hated wearing it especially when my friends saw me in it the majority of us were in the same predicament as us that's why I used to hate the song called Second Hand Rose.

A friend of mine a lady pensioner told me a true tale, once upon a time when she was a little girl twelve years of age she yearned for a pair of police clogs during that period the clog dance was all the range she went in to the bridal when the police inspector happened to glance up from his desk he saw her standing there looking so pitiful he asked her if she was lost "No Sir she replied but I would like a pair of clog shoes" He asked her for her name and address she told him he said that he would do his best for her well one evening a few days later a knock came at the door her Mother went to open it there was a policeman standing there she got such a shock thinking it was bad news she invited him in he told her that he had come to take down more details concerning her daughters request for a pair of clog shoes she was speechless for a while then she said to him "No thank you very much".

After the policeman had left she gave her daughter a good hiding saying that will teach you a lesson, they were very proud folks no matter how destitute they were police clothed were the last straw most of them would never accept charity they would rather go bare footed than be called names after people in the streets shouting, "You are wearing police clothes " The girls' police clothes were navy blue serge dresses grey thick ribbed socks and heavy steel toe cap clogs, the boys wore the same kind of clogs and serge blue trousers with a jacket to match and grey three quarter length ribbed socks some of the children were spiteful and would mock them, I was always petrified hoping I would never have to wear them.

I had a best friend in our class I wont' mention her real name lets call her Rose I used to take her home with me every afternoon after school, poor Rose her family were much poorer than we were she had socks with holed in and the soles of her shoes were padded with cardboard but that wasn't unusual in those days she was very pretty and such fun to be with Mum always made such a fuss of her she would give her a cuppa cocoa and a jam butty then she would search until she found an old pair of shoes an a clean old jumper for her to wear.

Saturday was always busy in most homes a lot of the women used to hang around the markets near closing time with some of their children while the stall holders were clearing away and disposing of all stuff that they didn't want on to the ground the children and women would go all around the pitches and stalls collecting all the thrown out stuff in to their bags or clean floured sacks they would pick up all the faded fruit and vegetables and potatoes they would cut away the faded parts wash them and make lovely fruit pies for Sunday tea if they had any fruit left over they would make jam'.

I remember me Dad telling me once that there were over three million men alone on the dole during that period they went on a hunger march, a large gigantic queue of them had to line up to receive hand outs of soup and bread that was given to them from some charity.

The night watchman called around every night to check how many people slept in your house the law was only four persons in one room folks used to take in some of their relatives and married couples who were homeless.

One little girl had to hide in the closet in their back yard during the sleet and snow until the watchman had gone her poor Mother was so anxious for she had completely forgotten all about her the little girl was crying loud let me out.

A pensioner I knew whose name is George once told me that during that period he was employed as an inspector in the workhouse what he saw brought tears to his eyes families that when they were first brought in had to be bathed with carbolic soap their hair was cut very, very short in case they caught head lice if they had caught them their head would be shaved completely bald they would be isolated nobody would go anywhere near them, they looked so pathetic it was a terrible sight to see them walking with their head bent down they hadn't had the facilities to bathe as they were destitute and broke, it wasn't the fashion then to have your head shaved so people kept their distance in case they caught them from them.

The children were separated from their parent' sisters and brothers they didn't know what it was all about the poor women were parted from their husbands a lot of them were pregnant, the poor defenceless ones were sobbing endlessly hanging on to their husbands arms they didn't want to be separated from their loved ones.

The warden would have to go and pull them apart, can you just imagine what t must have felt like for them try and visualize it happening to your family.

People would shudder at the thought of the workhouse because once you were in there it was impossible to come out again only with the exception of many of those who ran away or committed suicide.

The diet was very poor indeed the adults received ten ounces of meat a week if they were lucky the three meals consisted of hashed meat on Saturdays they were given watered down stew that comprised once ounce of beef and potatoes added to a gallon of water.

Good rations on the other hand were part of the working conditions of the staff at the workhouse although their pay was very low they were allowed more rations and a wide variety of food than the poor inmates who were in their care they were supplied with bread, butter, treacle, meat and many more food items that were a luxury.

On Christmas day as a rare treat the inmates were given roast beef potatoes vegetables and gravy for dessert they had plump pudding and custard this was only given to the elderly folks it was a very harsh life for all the inmates.

5

HAPPY DAYS

We moved from Bancroft Street to a four roomed council house in Myrtle Gardens we lived on the third landing it had a small kitchen a small bathroom and a medium size living room with a fireplace in the middle and an oven on one side for cooking, in the boys room there was a glass door that lead on to a verandah Mum and Tucker put small window boxes on the wall they both had green fingers, it was Mums' only pleasure in her spare time.

We had our meals in the living room on a large oak dinning table that could be drawn out at both sides for two more people to sit at. There was a black polished dressing table on one side of the living room in the centre of it was a large oval shaped mirror with two cupboards on both sides with two drawers, hanging on the walls side by side where two china plates with pictures of O' Donnell Street in Dublin, on the wall opposite where two beautiful pictures of a little girl and boy mending their fishing nets they were dressed in fisherman clothes wearing wellingtons and a fishermans hat perched on top of their head the girl looked as if she was sulking over a trivial matter on the other picture she is smiling as the boy glances up at her. Another lovely picture that Mum treasured was of a little boy with sky blue eyes, gorgeous golden curls dressed in a rich brown velvet suit wearing a white frilled collared shirt a brown bow-tie, three quarter knee length socks, black patent leather shoes with a silver buckle across the front of them.

Sunday morning after we arrived home from Mass and communion the girls had to take turn to stay in and help with the domestic work cleaning all the brass and tidying up the bedrooms, the boys were more fortunate because they didn't have to do any chores except on rare occasions to go on an errand.

If we needed a Doctor badly to come out and attend to any of us Mum would have to pay five-shillings it was a lot of money in those days so if we were sick Mum would cure us herself with her ancient herbal remedies.

There was never a dull moment in our house Dad would sometimes give me a bet to take for him to the bookie who was one of the neighbours who lived in the opposite block of flats to us he would write out his bet wrap the money up inside the paper if he won in the evening he would ask me to go and collect his winnings I would always tell me Mum if he won she used to tell him off for sending me but I loved going for him.

One of the men was the look out for the police so he could warn the bookie in time otherwise he would be arrested then he would have to appear in court maybe sentenced to prison.

Before I was born Mum and Dad lived in Orpie Street in Everton at weekends Dad used to go to the local pub called The Stingo majority of the regulars were prodestants I think me Dad was the only catholic, during that period people were very bitter concerning religion it didn't matter to me Dad the folks just accepted him as one of the regulars for he was an easy going chap with a great personality, it we ever had the blues he would cheer us up.

In May (1935) it was the coronation of King George the sixth and Queen Elizabeth, to celebrate the occasion there where street parties in all the streets in Liverpool it was sunny glorious happy day, all the roads, streets and houses were all decorated in colours of red, white and blue Mum made a beautiful garland of flowers with crepe paper and wire in the same colours she arranged them in a hanging basket and hung them over our front door all the streets had parties the children were presented with a china mug with a portrait of the coronation on the front of it, every one was happy and gay especially the children all siting around the party tables wearing their party dresses and hats eating ice-cream sandwiches, cakes, trifles and lemonade after the children's party had finished in the evening we sat on the doorsteps and kerbs watching the coupled dancing seeing all the coloured streamers swaying and the illuminated fairy lights it was a beautiful sight to behold.

The month of May was a memorial month for celebrations for us all we saw the first illuminated tramcar then there was the blossom trees in full bloom in colours of deep purple, lilac, pink and white the little girls would collect the fallen blossom to take home and put them in to a vase or a jam-jar, with the rose petals we would collect them and put them in to a tiny bottle with some water to make perfume the sun was scorching hot in those days it was absolutely brilliant all the children used to play out in the street the middle of the roads were thick with tar we used to burst all the tar bubbles with our fingers after we had finished our little game we would go home our hands covered in tar, Mum would give us a piece of margarine to rub on our hands to get rid of the tar.

After school we played games in the street skipping, hopscotch, marbles, jacks and hi -light bats, and ball shuttles rounder there was never a dull moment the boys played cricket and football pigeon toss with pennies and various games, when gooseberries were in season Mum would pie some to make a pie for Sunday tea I would ask her for some so would some of my friends ask their Mums for some also then we used to sit on the doorstep threading the gooseberries with a sewing needle and some thread to make necklets and bracelets.

A dear departed friend of mine named Lilian told me when she was a little girl her and her playmates would buy cherries after they had eaten them they saved the stones she washed and dried them placed them on a small baking tin and put them in to a warm oven until they looked like new wood, she put them in to small boxes and sold them a hundred half a penny some of her friends who never got pocket money would give them some for nothing so that they could join in the game which was trying to throw the cherry stones up in to an iron drain-pipe attached to the wall outside the house, the one who succeeded won the game and would be given all the cherry stones.

When I first started school there where two nuns sister Monica and sister Benedict they dressed in long black robes with a black thin head scarf a black nob pin to keep it on around their neck hung a large rosary beads with a silver and black crucifix down the centre of the robe black stockings and black serviceable shoes.

After they had introduced us to our teacher whose name was Miss Cunningham she was dressed in a brown tweed skirt a pale blue silk blouse wearing brown brogue shoes and brown silk stockings she had lovely auburn hair and lovely hazel coloured eyes and she wore spectacles she was a lovely caring teacher.

Inside of the classroom where small wooden desks there was a blackboard and easel in the centre of the room by the wall some sticks of chalk and a rubber out block, on the right side was the teachers table with a vase filled with lovely flowers and foliage and her chair, on the other wall hung drawings and pictures.

We had lots of picture books to read and toys to play with I made friends with a nice girl called Annie Fox and Nellie Walker Nellies mother passed away when Nellie was just a little girl she was brought up with her Grandmother. As I began to grow up I started taking school more serious we were taught Latin catechism

English arithmetic poetry reading sewing drama sports and folk dancing my favourite subjects were sports cookery drama sewing and folk dancing.

If we were disobedient we were given a slap on the hand with a thin wooden ruler by the teacher but if we continued being disobedient we were sent along to the room where the nuns occupied then we would be given the cane, on the palms of your hands it was very painful your palms would sting terribly.

I wasn't very happy in Miss Morgan's class where we taught catechism and Latin she was very strict if you couldn't memorise the lesson she would give you a hard rap on your knuckles I loved the drama class taught by Miss Gill we all adored her she looked like a film star with her lovely walk and her petite figurer and her firey red hair and sea green eyes it was great fun being in her class once I was in a play called 'Pilgrims Progress' I played the character of The Wife of Bath I can still recall my line 'Ah here come more children for our holy shrine'.

Later I entered Miss Sheppards class she taught us crafts she was a lovely teacher one afternoon I was in the cloakroom getting ready to go home when she entered the cloakroom she gave me a beautiful blue bathing costume and a silver coloured bathing cap I was over the moon as I was longing to learn how to swim but Mum couldn't afford to buy me one, I thanked her sincerely she was for ever given us some nice cast off clothes.

My first lesson at learning to swim was in Lodge Lane public baths it was a disaster the pool was a bit deep so I just floated about with one hand on the bar suddenly someone pushed me in to the water it was very deep for me it scared me call it what you may after that episode I gave up learning to swim. Miss Sheppard also taught us nature study I loved it sometimes she took on nature walks through the park it was heavenly.

Miss Bold was our dancing teacher she was magnificent she was like a fairy on her feet she had an old fashion gramophone with a horn attached to it she used to play it for us while we practised our folk dancing.

Sometimes on our way back to school after lunch time we would see a group of musicians and dancers they were men dressed up as women we loved watching them dancing and singing and doing their acrobats we would follow them through the streets near by us we got carried away then we would forget the time and be late returning to school.

When it was the last week of term after all of the pencils and books had been collected we would wash out all the cupboards in the classroom then the teacher would tell us to go and empty all the waste paper baskets and dispose of the books papers stub pencils paints etc there would be scrambles at the bins as we searched for all kinds of articles such as drawings paints paper flowers and all kinds that we had disposed of and our prizes.

Preparing for Easter was great fun in school we made bunny rabbits chicks Easter baskets and Easter cards and egg cosies, we had new clothes black patient leather ankle-band shoes white socks pretty flowered dresses and pinafores blazers and lovely coloured hair ribbons.

The boys would also be rigged out with new clothes and shoes no matter how poor our parents were through no fault of their own they always made certain that we enjoyed our Easter holiday.

There was never a dull moment, in the streets you would hear the cries of vendors selling their wares, an Indian man used to come around selling home made Indian toffee he carried a small tin box that hung around his shoulders on a thick leather strap he had a bell that he used to ring, all the children would come running out to buy some toffee from him, it cost half a penny for a small bag full it tasted simply delicious it melted in your mouth.

Another man came around selling cockles and mussles and kewins, after the children had bought some if it was a nice fine day they would sit on their front door step picking the kewins out of their shells with a pin and eating them. Then there was the ice-cream man and various other vendors.

A man and woman used to come around the man played the bar-rel organ while the lady danced there would be crowds of folks watching them after they had completed their performance the man went around to all of the spectators, with his cap in his hand collecting coppers from them.

There was 'The One Man Band' he was absolutely famous he travelled to Canada and various other countries to play, when I was a little girl I used to follow him all around and ask him to play 'When Irish Eyes Are Smiling' while he played it for me I would sing and dance merrily all around I was always excited waiting for him to come to our street.

There was the pigeon man he usually came around on Sunday afternoons carrying his pigeon basket made of thick wooden cane with a silver lock attached to it inside the basket where lots of pigeons, all the children would gather around him he would unlock the basket then all the pigeons would fly away to the Pier Head we would stand by him waiting patiently for them to return back to him which they always did.

Some Sunday afternoons if Mum and Dad could afford the fare they would take us to New Brighton or to Seacombe taking sand-wiches and home made lemonade carrying our buckets and spades and an empty jam-jar to catch frogs and tadpoles, the fare was tuppence return we would clamber excitedly on board the boat as it was crossing the River Mersey the sun would be glittering on the water you could feel the taste of the salty water as it splashed against your face, the white foam on the water as the engine of the boat was sailing the seagulls flying high above the misty pale blue sky, the sea breeze blowing it was exhilarating, When we arrived at our destination immediately we would take off our shoes and socks and start making sand castles some of us would go searching for frogs and tadploes and sea shells we fill the jar with sea water and some sea weed, around the brim of the jar was a piece of string made in to a handle to carry the jar to take home with us.

On Sunday August Bank holidays Mum and Dad always treated us to New Brighton one time she made a quart bottle of home made lemonade after we arrived at New Brighton I became quite thirsty as Mum handed me the bottle to pour some out the bottle slipped out of my hands rolled down the ground and smashed to pieces all the children were crying for a drink so me Dad went to the shop to buy a bottle of real lemonade.

Returning home after a lovely days outing we would all climb on top of the deck of the boat, watching the sunrise and the waves splashing against the sides of the boat, when we arrived home we would have a lovely tea then we would all be ready for bed as the sea air had knocked us all out.

Some Sundays after we had attended Mass providing that the weather was nice me Dad would take us to Princess Park while Mum prepared the Sunday roast dinner In the centre of the park there was a field opposite the lake where the ducks and swans swam, Dad told us that in the field many years ago there was a pony named Judy, Judy had a trap in which about twelve children would ride in it Judy would take them for a joy ride around the field in the pony trap. He showed us Judy's burial place in the field, all the children use to put buttercups daisies and dandelions and tree branches at the foot of Judy's resting-place, some of the children still keep up the ritual today, if you pass by you will always see some wild flowers by the grave of Judy, on Judy's headstone there is a epitaph written on a stone this is what it says,

IN MEMORY OF JUDY
WHO
DURING 21 YEARS SERVICE
IN THIS PARK WAS
THE CHILDRENS FRIEND
DIED 12th AUGUST 1926
AGED 26 YEARS

Judy's Grave

At the entrance of Sefton Park was a marble statue attached to it was a thick steel chain with a small drinking cast iron cup below was a tap, it was a novelty to all the children we would stand on tip toe to get a drink of water, then we would listen to the birds chirping merrily away, then me Dad would take us all through the park, the blossom trees were in full bloom the fragrance was heavenly there where lots of wild flowers in the centre of the field Dad always picked a bunch of them to take home for Mum.

Some Sunday afternoons we would go to benediction to St Anne's church as we were retuning home, on entering our house the aroma was breath taking with the smell of Mum's home made fruit pies, scones, potato cakes egg custards and bread she was a marvellous cook.

After tea if the weather was fine we would play games outside, in the evening the women and men would a game of "Tug of War" with a long thick rope all of the children would be sitting on the front doorsteps cheering them on we would be so excited wondering, which side was going to win the winners got a big round of applause.

A lot of the children attended Cob Hall in the evening once a week it was a bible class study, it didn't matter what religion you were every one was welcome, we were all given a small bible picture card with a verse printed on it some of us were asked to stand up an say a verse from our card, all of us would sit there waiting patiently for the class to end because we would all receive a lovely cup of cocoa and a big fresh jam cob, that is how it got the name Cob Hall my verse was,

> "The wages of sin is death
> But the gift of God
> Is eternal life forever" Amen.

Mum didn't have any social life with all the family she had to take care of, I recall one evening she took me to see a film called 'Nellie Kelly' it was a beautiful Irish film when ever mum sang the baby to sleep hugging the baby in a shawl to he bosom sometimes she would sing the song 'Nellie Kelly' she had a sweet soft lilting voice.

During the winter time in the evenings we would go and visit the Cockney Watchman he was the watchman for the road repairs, when there where tramcars, he had a small wooden hut with a lovely blazing coal-fire, where he used to sit all the children would gather around it warming their hands, he would put potatoes on top of the fire to bake then he would give us one each in turn.

One Friday afternoon after school, in our house we were playing a game of 'Fish and Chips' sitting around the dinning table cutting up pieces of old newspapers in to large pieces and small ones, making believe they were fish and chips we would pretend to put salt and vinegar on them and wrap them up and sell them to our customers one of us would be the shop assistant the rest of us were customers, for money we used bonny-mug which was small pieces of broken crockery.

Me Dad was working in Grove Street at that time on repairing the tram-car lines the men used to get paid late on Friday afternoons, mum sent one of us along to go and collect his wages from him because she didn't have any money to get the messages for his tea, after receiving his wages she placed them on the dinning table, while she went to get her shawl and her shopping basket on her return she told us to clear away the mess and tidy up as we swept and tidied up we threw all the bits of paper in to the fire, unfortunately the fire was lit when Mum went to pick up the wage packet off the table it had disappeared she was frantic we searched everywhere but couldn't find it she said that one of us must have thrown it in to the fire by mistake, she was almost certain of it she said that if she ever caught us playing 'Fish and Chip Shop' again we would be in serious trouble.

One of our neighbours used to sell roast potatoes and spare ribs and cabbage sometimes Mum would send us on this errand with a basin to put the food in, most of the children were always eager to go on this errand for their parents because, the lady who cooked and sold the food would always give us a roast potato that we thoroughly enjoyed eating on our way home.

The 'Rag and Bone' man used to come around the streets crying out any old rags the poor folks would come running out with their worn out clothes or anything else they could find in exchange for them he would give them a few coppers.

Sometimes I used to go to the swing park after school had ended with my friend Annie, unknown to me Mum of course one afternoon there was Annie spinning high up over the may-pole swing while the rest of us girls all pulled out on our chains I couldn't resist having a go there I was spinning high up in the air, when suddenly my hand slipped I fell to the ground with such a band I could hardly walk the pain in my right ankle was so server I hobbled home with assistance from my friend, mum gave me such a scolding going to the swing park my ankle began to swell badly I couldn't put my foot down when she saw the swelling and pain that I was suffering she told me Dad to take me to the Children's hospital in Myrtle Street he carried me on his shoulders all the way there, it wasn't too far from where we lived.

They x-rayed my ankle after the results they told me Dad that I had n my kle-bone the nurse then set it in plaster –paris. We always had duck apple night it was great fun Mum and Dad would put a bowl of cold water on the table with apples inside of the apples were pennies and with our with our hands behind our backs and blind folded, in turns we would duck in to the bowl with our mouth and try to bite an apple after the game ended Dad would put chestnuts on a small shovel place the shovel on to the red coal-fire to roast them for us to eat.

Mayday was a very special occasion also an annual holiday, all the carters came to town for the Mayday procession with their horses, ponies, donkies and dogs their carriages were gaily deco-rated with lovely flowers and pretty assorted coloured ribbons, the animals were also gaily dressed up, ribbons were attached to the manes of the horses and donkies and ponies, the clowns and harlequins accompanied them, the parade was usually held in Sefton Park all the children would dance merrily around the may-pole, it was a beautiful sight to behold.

The last Mayday procession that I saw was in (1989) in Sefton Park it reminded me of Victorian times there where carters with their horse drawn carriages and wagon one carriage that I saw was a sky blue colour lined with rich blue velvet and fringed with gold braided tassels around the edges, it carried six passengers on both sides of the carriage where oil lamps with the wicks still inside of the lamps, the riding throng was made of leather with colours of red and black on the handle, there was a head cover on top of the carriage so that it could be opened or closed depending on the weather.

Some of the carriages dated back to (1838) with advertisements printed on them for hiring them out for weddings and other spe-cial occasions there was a Webster wagon with beer barrels on it, printed on the wagon was this

'The Home Brewing Excellence (1852)
and a
Tetley Walker First Est (1852)

All of the wagons had horses attached to them, with their beauti-ful long manes weaved in to long plaits tied back with pretty assorted coloured ribbons there where colts and ponies decorated with flowers, some of the children where gathered around them feeding them with grass.

As the sun was exceedingly hot that Saturday afternoon, I saw one of the owners covering his pony with a coat of red and white trying to protect the pony from the scorching sun then he walked it under a tree in to the shade.

I asked one of the owners the names of his ponies, they were named Smartie, Peanuts, Rambler, and Pippins I was fascinated by the tiny dog he owned named Sandy it had a light brown coat with a tiny spec of snow white around its neck it kept walking around and around the two horses, the owner told me that they were one happy family, the eldest horse was called Uncle the other horse was named Nephew and that Sandy had lived with them since she was a pup.

Standing beside one of the horse drawn carriage was the May Queen she looked breath taking with her sea blue eyes her long blonde ringlets adorning her hair and her pale complexion elegantly dressed in a white satin long dress edged with lace wearing a grown and with white accessories to match, a bouquet of flowers in her hands sitting inside the horse drawn carriage were four little girls dressed as bridesmaids, they wore long satin lilac dresses lilac stockings and lilac satin shoes and tiny lilac satin handbags trimmed with sequins and holding posies in one hand. There where policemen in uniform wearing decorative headdress, they were having their photos taken, some were posing standing by a horse, some with a child sitting on their lap some just standing there by a horse drawn carriage and some posing by their police horse.

There where lots of stalls selling souvenirs and posters with the Horse Prayer printed on the poster, the children and adults were all enjoying their selves immensely having pony rides and to end it all there was a barbecue selling baked potatoes in their jackets, beef burgers salad fruit drinks and ice-cream all at reasonable prices.
The sun was shinning down brightly now it was just like being in

the country with the breeze blowing gently it reminded me of the evacuation. I spotted two shire horses one named Robin the other one named Charles, their bells were jingling on their harness their long black manes were pleated and dressed with ribbons in rasta colours of red, green and gold they were decorated with beautiful lemon, red and pale pink roses and they wore carnations of red, white and pink.

I fed Robin some grass he glanced up at me with his brown eyes then, he rubbed his foot gently upon the grass I overheard some one telling their child that when they rub their foot they are talking in the animal language.

After the owners took their horses harness off they took them under a tree to rest and cool off.

There where two lovely lady horse riders dressed in their riding habits wearing snow white shirts back leather suits knee length riding boots with black velvet hats and holding a riding throng.

Along came a pony trap cart the cart was full of hay sitting inside the cart were four people and the driver, they looked like Gypsies then I saw a shire carriage a shinny black colour, painted on the cab in bold gold letters were the words "IMAGEN " what a lovely gesture I thought for John Lennon I presumed.

There where two adorable shetland ponies one named sunshine it coat was a sunny golden colour, theother pony standing by was called Sheep its coat was a lovely bluey black, the smoke rising from the barbecue, the children happily waiting to be served it was a memorial day for it took me back to my childhood.

6
PADDY'S MARKET

On Saturday afternoons Mum would take each one of us in turn with her to Paddy's market I loved going with her it still exits today, there are pitches stalls and shops that sell new and second hand clothes and shoes and any other articles that you require, their far much cheaper than you can buy any where else.

When I was a little girl I remember one Saturday afternoon when I went with Mum to Paddy's market I saw a lovely pair of second hand black patent leather ankle band shoes they were all the fashion then and I had been longing for a pair of them for ages imagine my delight when Mum told me to try them on, they felt a bit tight at the toes I squeezed them on when Mum asked me if they fitted me I said yes they do she paid a few coppers for them which was a lot of money then, I was so thrilled I couldn't wait for Monday to come for me to go to school to show them off to my friends.

One bitterly cold winters Saturday afternoon a few weeks just before Christmas I went with Mum to Paddy's market, snow flakes began to fall twirling gentry to the ground the Salvation Army band were playing and singing Christmas carols while Mum and I were mooching for bargains suddenly a pretty little girl appeared she had beautiful golden girls, emerald green eyes clad in a thin haggardly frock she was bare footed that was not unusual to see during that period it reminded me of the story of Oliver Twist.

Paddy's Market

Mum beckoned the little girl over to her side she sort out a pair of second hand shoes and told the girl to try them on they fitted her nicely Mum asked the price of them after she had paid for them and with a big smile we watched her as she walked happily away, that was Mum she always cared for the poor waifs and strays.

Mary Ellen's standing by their pitches or stalls shouting out selling their merchandise watching out for the thieves and vagabonds, majority of the Mary Ellen wore thick woollen shawls around their shoulders and men's caps upon their heads as it was perishing cold with all the wide open space and no roof in the market, I remember one the Mary Ellen's telling me that one Saturday morning when the priest from St Anthony's church came to pay them a visit seven of them were friends from childhood days he always called the Magnificent

The market stretched for miles crowds of people always went there to search for bargains no matter what the weather was like it was a fun days outing for them, a lot of Indian seamen went there when they were on shore leave some of the traders used to raise the prices up to them you would hear them bargaining with each other.

On the way home from Paddy's market Mum would take me with her in to St Anthony's church it was only five minutes from the market, she would light a penny candle then she would put a copper in St Anthony's bread box for the poor the money that was collected was distributed amongst the waifs and strays and the homeless.

Most of the Catholics always went in to St Anthony's church on their way home from the market to pray for a special intention and to light a penny candle, it was just like a feast day on Saturday afternoon there would be at least a hundred candles lit flickering and blowing in the wind each time the church door was

St Anthony's Church

opened yet they never went out it reminded me of a grotto.

After coming out of church Mum would take us for a special treat across the road to a workman's café called The Cocoa Rooms, all the professional Mary Ellen washer women went after they had finished work in the public wash house they would have a bowl of hot home-made rich pea soup and a piece of fresh crusty bread for afters they had steamed pudding and creamy custard, it was warm and snuggy on a winters day, for us Mum would order lovely home made steak and kidney pudding mashed potatoes mushy peas with lovely thick gravy for dessert we would have jam rolly polly with delicious thick creamy custard or suet pudding with custard after I had finished and thanked her she would say "Don't' let your Father know as he will think I've got lots of money she was a good provider she never ever spent a penny on herself yet she always looked immaculately clean and tidy looking.

Now the best part of Saturday afternoon was around four o clock my young brother Tucker and I would be sent on an errand to a first class confectionery shop called Kirkland Jennings in Beaconfield street I would carry a large white flour sack, nearly all the poor children went on the same errand there would be a huge queue outside the shop when it came to my turn I would ask for six pennyworth of stale bread it wasn't stale but as it was weekend it had to be sold so it came as quite a bargain, the smell of the cake shop was delicious my mouth would be watering in to my flour sack the shop assistant would put a large cottage loaf a large hovis loaf, a large currant loaf a couple of currant buns some broken biscuits and a few cakes, she always gave us a whole cake each that we would eat on our way home Tucker never liked the idea of going with me.

Saturday nights there was a lot of activities going on first after Dad and our brothers went out to the local for a pint we had a

bath in front of the coal fire Mum filled the tin bath with hot water then we would have a cosy bath.

When we ready for bed just as the pubs were closing we could hear them all returning home singing to the top of their voices in the street they would be carrying jars of ale that they had a whip round for as our they entered our house Mum would have a large plate of sandwiches ready for them to eat we would sit on the stairs listening to them having a holey dancing and singing in turn they would end up having a good old knees up Mum was quite the opposite to me Dad he was a song and dance man, while Mum was quite the opposite she was on the more on the reserved side she would tell him to slow, when some of the men got drunk they would knock their poor wives about they didn't mean to hurt them they just couldn't bear the thought of not being able to provide for their wives and children, during the depression in the (1930's) they would plead with their wives to forgive them, a lot of men committed suicide they weren't strong enough to live that way.

7

GRAN O'DONNELL

Gran O' Donnell was my grandmother she was me Dads mother, we called her Ganny she married rather late in years. I'm not certain of her age but she lived to be about eighty. She was a professional dancer and she also performed on the Gaiety Theatre near Scotland road she was a very strong person.

Two years after her and Grandy had moved in to their new home she became pregnant later on she gave birth to a beautiful baby girl who was born crippled, she was christened Harriet she didn't live long a year later Ganny gave birth to another lovely baby girl she passed away not long after she was born, poor Ganny was broken hearted during that period hundreds of new born babies died after childbirth it was due mostly to malnutrition it wasn't their parents fault.

A year after Ganny became pregnant again this time she gave birth to a baby boy he was baptised George after his father, twelve months later she bore another baby boy who was baptised James after her long lost brother in America, as the boys grew up they became very close to each other George was quite distinguished with a Romany look about with his jet blue black thick hair, deep set blue eyes, James was quite the reverse. He was more of an intellect he had lovely auburn hair sky blue eyes.

Grandy always gave Ganny all of his earnings she would give him back a few coppers pocket money, he would walk all the way to his destination in stead of travelling on the tram-car to save his coppers to buy fruit or sweets for his sons.

At bedtime Grandy would teach his sons to say "The Lords Prayer" in Gae'lic in the Welsh language Ganny would interrupt him saying that he wasn't saying it properly because it sounded different to her but that was Ganny she was contrary her and Grandy were like chalk and cheese.

When George and James had been at school for a while they began to play truant until one day the school board caught up with them their parents didn't know anything about the episode, later on they were taken in to care and sent to a boys home called St Edwards there George learnt to play the bugle he was brilliant at it they nick named him The Bugle Boy. After they returned home they both decided to join the army when they broke the news to their parents they were deeply moved the brothers made certain their parents were well provided for while they where away as Ganny and Grandy bid them farewell at the train station they were deeply upset, they both served in the (1914) war James was wounded one half of his ear was blown off and George was deeply wounded in his knee, while all this had occurred Grandy had suddenly became very ill and passed away poor Ganny was left all alone in a deep state of shock.

When the lads were demobbed and had returned home they found their Mother waiting patiently with open arms for them at the station ready to greet them they had not been notified of their Fathers death Ganny gently broke the sad news to them they were utterly speechless and emotionally upset.

Ganny was never the same after losing Grandy the lads did their very best to comfort her they even bought her a pup they named it Prince she wasn't too keen on it at first, gradually it started following her everywhere as it began to grow it began performing all kinds of tricks, when Ganny went shopping she never took a shopping bag instead she would tie a spotless white apron around her waist and put all her shopping inside of the apron, sometimes she would go to the local pub called The Brown Cow at the corner of Crown street and upper Parliament street she loved a drop of Guinness Prince would trot behind her in to the pub then curl up under Gannys chair, when she was ready to leave Prince would get up then trot after her as she left the pub.

On the twelfth of July when the Orange Lodge was on parade, Prince would trot behind the Irish Pipers barking like mad it was the same with Prince on St Patrick's day he would do the same thing all the children loved Prince especially Ganny.

Ganny was a rare character indeed with such a striking personality with her deep set blue eyes that had a twinkle in them she could see right through you and tell you your fortune also she was very out spoken she was quite regal looking she had a tan complexion jet blue black long thick hair streaked with a slight touch of silver grey it was weaved in a thick braid plait and rolled around the crown of her head like a coronet pinned to the back of her plait was a large tortoise–shell fan comb studded with brilliant imitation pearls, she wore soft black leather three quarter knee-length lace up boots thick black stockings her dress was a gaily coloured skirt a silk black and white shirt blouse with a pillar box red petticoat underneath wrapped around her shoulders hung a beautiful silk fringed shawl with colours of the rainbow printed on it, tied around her waist was a two-bib stall pocket like the one that the stall holders used to wear in Paddy's market, inside one of the pockets she kept an small old empty mustard tin inside was her pinch of fine Irish snuff in the other pocket was her rosary beads I can always picture her sitting in her old rocking chair with her rosary beads in one hand saying the rosary I would be getting up to all kinds of mischief in her bedroom she would stamp her foot giving me a little scolding then she would continue saying the rosary.

On one of her fingers she wore a solid gold keepers ring it had two tiny diamonds embodied in the centre on the other finger she wore her wedding ring.

I was christened Brigita after Ganny I was called Bridie for short, some of the girls in our class at school used to tease me calling me Biddy I hated that name I would go home to see Ganny after school when I told her about the teasing she would band her first on the table and say to me that Brigita is a fine old Irish name.

In the autumn as soon as dusk began to appear Ganny would light two small kerosene lamps that stood on either side of the mantle-piece I would be looking out of her living room window patiently waiting for the lamp-lighter to appear to light all the street lamps, with a long stick in one hand then he would gently pull the chain on the gas-mantle to light the lamps, sometimes in the nice fine weather the little girls would tie a thick rope to the lamp post and have a lovely swing.

Saturday mornings I always went over to Gannys' to clean the passage and the front door step I would sandstone the step it was a ritual. She loved a wee drop of whiskey she called it her medicine it helped to relieve her bad rheumatism, sometimes she would ask me to go to the snug for her she would wrap her Mary Ellen shawl around my shoulders and give me her small medicine bottle and the money, she would tell me to walk straight through to the snug room and ask for a wee dram of whiskey for her, children were not allowed to be served but the publican knew it was for Ganny.

I loved mooching I still do in her bedroom she kept an old fashion black trunk underneath her bed, I would rummaged through it, it contained lots of fineries gorgeous silk fringed shawls and lots of accessories and the most beautiful picture hats adorned with various pastel coloured satin ribbons some hats were adorned with large fine coloured feathers the rest had pretty flowers attached to them.

I loved dressing up in them when Ganny realised I was missing she would call out "What are you doing in there Minnie the Moocher? She gave me that nick name as I was always mooching.

On the first Friday of each month the priest always came and gave Ganny Holy Communion the evening before he came she would scrub the dinning table then early Friday morning she would place a snow white Irish linen tablecloth edged with fine lace on to the table, then place a candlestick with a candle inside just as the priest arrived she would light the candle, he would hold a small silver crucifix then he would begin the mass and Ganny would receive Holy Communion I was fascinated just watching the service after the mass had ended the priest would say to her "Come on now Brigita don't be hiding the whiskey she would go straight to the cabinet take out two small glasses and the small bottle of whiskey that she always reserved for special occasions and pour out a small amount after she had handed him a glass she would say to him just a wee drop to warm the cockles of your heart.

Gerry my older brother lived with Ganny she idolised him and spoilt him terribly her was her favourite, she always cooked him roast potatoes and baked beans, if he happened to be on the scene when she was having one of her tantrums he knew just how to calm her down he would tease her by saying to her, shall I put Athlone on the radio for you because she loved that radio station she loved the Irish music that was played she would start tapping her feet to it.

St Patrick' day was very special to her and to all of us she would buy my sisters and me pretty green pinafores to wear over our frocks then she would pin a small Irish harp on us that she had made they were made up in various beautiful shades of green, with hand sewn sequins attached to them, on her kitchen window sill she would place a small glass jam-jar with water inside and a bunch of shamrock so that you could see it as you passed by her window along the landing.

When the Irish Pipers came around playing their Irish music to celebrate that day parading through all the streets in Liverpool Ganny would be gaily dancing in front of the band with her dog Prince trotting behind her barking merrily away and all the children and adults they would follow the band for miles and miles, until evening time the grown ups would end up in the pubs. One of our neighbours told us that Ganny once worked in the Rope works in Lodge Lane one day, while all the staff were busy working the radio was playing some Gipsy music Ganny leaped up on to a table and started dancing the Flamingo showing of all her gaily coloured petticoats twirling around and around and clapping her hands to them music the in walked the Works Manager he said to them all "Come on now every body the show is over back to work" she got such a loud applause.

When Ganny hade a drop too much to drink we would try to get her to lie down in her bedroom oh what a performance we had we would loosen all her clothes then undo the laces in her ankle boots eventually we would succeed while all this was going on she would be singing in her own fashion gradually she would fall fast asleep.

One Saturday morning when I went over to see her not long after I had arrived she asked me if I would go to the snug for her? I didn't feel like going as it was such a beautiful sunny day I wanted to play outside with my friends, she started saying that her chest was paining her, I thought she was just putting on an act so I would go for her whiskey as it was one of her tricks I didn't know that this time she was being serious otherwise I would have run like lightening later on she called me and told me to go upstairs and ask her friend Mrs Day to come down as soon as possible after Mrs Day arrived, there was a lot of commotion going on then Mum and Dad came over then the Doctor came Mum told me to go outside and not to come back in until I was told, I remember seeing Auntie Mary coming over in the evening I saw the Doctor leaving I went in to Gannys' I saw me Dad standing in front of the fire-guard tears flowing down his cheeks suddenly I knew something terrible had happened Ganny had passed away, it was at the same time as the Snug bar where she used to send me for her wee dram of whiskey it was right opposite her house was I was too young to attend her funeral I just stood watching Mum had kept me off from school to help out she gave me a pound note to pay the rent to the landlord well I went downstairs to the swings on the ground, I loved going on them I was swinging merrily away on the swinging boat with the pound note clutched in my hand I hadn't noticed that a gust of wind had swept the pound note clean out of my hand as I got off the swinging boat I realised that I had lost the money I started to panic then I began to cry, my friends tried to console me it was useless suddenly one of them came up with an idea they went knocking on all the doors in our block of flats saying "Please can you spare a few coppers Bridie Jones has lost her Mothers rent money" they exaggerated a little bit they collected about twelve-shillings and sixpence they put the money into a clean white ankle-sock and gave it to me saying "Don't' cry Bridie give this money to your Mum".

I was so upset I could hardly say thanks, then I happened to see my young brother Tucker walking along whistling, he asked me what all the commotion was about I told him then I asked him would he go and take the money over to Mum in Gannys house where she had been attending to her funeral seeing the coppers in the ankle-sock he refused to take it I didn't blame him either.

After a while I began to pluck up some courage I went over with it myself I kept wishing that Ganny was here she would have saved me instead I had to face the battle alone, when I handed Mum the ankle-sock with the money inside then I blurted out the story she was very annoyed with me she said "If it wasn't for your Grandmother passing away she would have punished me especially when she heard what my friends had done for me knocking on neighbours doors, I missed Ganny so much especially weekends we would all want to go and stay with her she never turned the children away if they had been thrown out in to the streets, cold and hungry with no where else to go she would bring tem in and feed them and let them stay she was deeply missed by us all when she passed away.

This is a very letter to me from Gannys' niece Maggie Crozier she passed away recently she was a lovely lady.

1 Grange Court
Off Grange Terrance
High St
Liverpool 15 8HA

Dear Bridie
I am sorry I have not answered your letter before now but I have not been too well I am afraid I can't help you about my Grandad as I never met him my eldest sister Mary was the only one whom did, and I believe he used to make a fuss of her and bring her new laid eggs she must have been his favourite, I think he must have had a farm somewhere, I would have loved to have met him also my Grandma but we were born to late Dolly and I. My Mother his daughter was a roman catholic and she married my Dad who used to play in a pipe and drum band in the Orange Lodge, and they were happy, but one of my Mothers sister was very bigoted and

did not like my Mother marrying a protestant, but Auntie Bridget your Granma was not at all bigoted she was a very humorous woman Dolly and I, loved going to see her and we also went to see your Mother also as they lived in the same house, your Mother was a lovely caring woman and she always made us very welcome, you have lost a good Mother when you lost her, the last time I saw her was at Dr Goldburgs Surgery in Myrtle St, and she looked ill then.

Your Grandma I think had a daughter but she died young so she only had your Dad and James, your Dad was very quiet, and tall whereas James was smaller they had nicknamed him Dabba, and I can remember him coming home covered in coal dust doing casual work for a few paltry wages. Auntie Bridget was a case she used to like her drink and she used to ask me to go with her for her shopping but no shopping bags for her, instead she tied a spotless white apron around her waist and put all her goods in, and there was a pub named Bob Tegins at the corner of Crown St and upper Parliament St, she got me to undo the apron and tie it somehow and mind it till she came out of the pub I think she liked her Guinnisis afterwards we would go home to her little parlour and I would make us both a cuppa and she gave me a shilling and that was a lot of money in them days, she did not like the women next door to her, she called her a snob, so when I called to see her after school she said I am glad you came Agraw I believe that is an endearing name in Irish, but I want you to measure my window, and go to Deans the Drapers in Smithdown Lane and buy me some pretty cre-tonne which I manage to do, and sew them up, she said tat woman next door wont' show me up when I put them up I must say the window did look nice, I must have been very old for my age as I think I was only about 9, but your Grandma was very humorous and she was very kind heart-ed, she was very good to us when we lost our Mum do you remember the long stone lobby when we were young Dolly and I used to scrub it on our hands and knees, no wonder I have rheumatics in my bones but we enjoyed doing it as we always ended up with some money of her, but we would have helped without her giving us any money as she was such a kind Auntie she married a protestant we kids used to call him Uncle Joney he was a quiet man , I wish I could have helped you more, but I do know I was born off Mill Street so maybe that is where your Great Grandfather lived if only you decided to write about him while my eldest sister was living she could have told you lots but Dolly and I were to young.

Well look after yourself and I hope you will soon feel better give my love to all the family.
Cheerio for now
Aunty Mag.

p.s. Please excuse the bad writing, and mistakes.
What are you studying at collage.

8

THE EVACUATION

When I was a little girl we lived in Myrtle Gardens on the first landing. Gran O' Donnell and Uncle Jim lived next door, there where swings downstairs all the children used to play on them,

most of them attended St Ann' school. One day I heard Mum talking to me Dad it wasn't intentionally I will tell you about it later in my true story.

A few years after we moved across to a block of flats but still in Myrtle Gardens as our family was increasing. Right opposite where we lived from our living room window we could see right across to Crown Street and look straight in to Martindales coal yard, sometimes we would watchthelads and men queuing up outside anxiously waiting to see if they would be fortunate enough to obtain a casual day job, then they would weigh up the coal and put it in to a coal sack and load it on to the coal wagon.

On September the third war was declared with Germany a broadcast came on the radio, from that time onwards everywhere had to be in total darkness any one showing any light would be in serious trouble, the air raid warden would go around checking to see that no lights were showing, as it would attract the German planes the people used torches and candles, of an evening all the windows had to be properly covered up.

We were all issued with identity cards and gas masks the gas masks were kept in a small cardboard box with a piece of string attached to it as a handle you carried it on your shoulder in case of emergency, I remember the first time I tried mine on the smell of the rubber was horrible I couldn't breathe properly.

We were issued with ration books for food clothing shoes etc the black market racketeers became very rich selling liquor, cigarettes nylons clothing coupons etc, one day while Mum was queuing up for bread outside the bakers shop she overheard a woman saying that she didn't mind the war as it had made her rich, Mum was so annoyed with her she gave her a good telling her that the black market may have made her rich but there where women who had sons and daughters and husbands fighting and that a lot of them had been killed or wounded or missing in action, she soon quietened down.

Anderson air raid shelters were built for people who wished to use them for protection when the bombs and shrapnel were falling, the shelters were made of concrete and steel inside of them were small wooden bunks for us to lie down or to just sit on, as soon as the people heard the wailing of the sirens to inform them that it was an air raid warning, folks would quickly pickup their torches and blankets and flasks of tea and go hurrying down the stairs in to the shelters, when they had settled down they would have a good old sing song to keep up their spirits everyone would join in singing, one of their favourite songs was,

"There'll be blue birds over
The white cliffs of Dover
Tomorrow just you wait and see
There'll' be love and laughter
And peace here after
Tomorrow when the world is free
The shepherd will tend his sheep
The valley will bloom again and Jimmy will go to sleep
In his own little room again
There'll' joy and laughter and peace ever after
Tomorrow just you wait and see.

Sang by the Forces sweetheart Vera Lynn.

The new occupants who moved into the house that we had moved from, were named Thomas they had a daughter named Jean who was in the same class as me we became good friends, one night the air raid started her they didn't go down in to the shelter her parents sheltered her and the rest of the family in a cupboard in the passage of their house, suddenly a bomb hit the block of flats the floorboards collapsed and they were trapped underneath the debris my Dad tried to force his way in to try and save them he could hear their cries pleading for help the authorities forbid him to enter as it was far too dangerous they all died, it was a terrible disaster.

Mum never did like that house she always used to say that the passage had a dark gloom about it remember do you remember I said earlier on that I heard Mum talking tome Dad one day well, she was telling him that Ganny kept telling her to move from that house Mum thought her mind must be wandering but Ganny must have had a premonition.

During the world war in (May 1941) Lord Haw Haw from Germany broadcasted on the radio everyday and night he would begin by saying "Germany calling Germany calling this is Lord Haw Haw speaking then he would name the town that they were going to bomb that night he was deadly serious about it that same night that same night that town would be completely bombed to ruins.

One night he broadcasted saying that they were going to bomb Liverpool to pieces, which they did the air raid lasted for seven consecutive nights it was called The Merseyside Raid the whole of the sky was lit up blazing red like fire.

One Sunday night during that long raid I was staying with a relative named Dolly Tasker, her husband James was away serving in the army she was living alone with her baby Jean it was Mums' idea for me to stay with her to keep her company. Suddenly the sirens began wailing, Dolly lived on the first landing she never went down in to the shelter so we took cover underneath the dinning table to escape the blast of the shrapnel from the bombs that were falling, we could hear the screams of some of the neighbours as they went dashing down the stairs to the shelters as the heavy bombardment of bombs and shrapnel Were falling from the German planes.

Uncle Jim lived on the same landing as Dolly they were first cousins we all thought that he had been killed when his house was bombed, later he was found by one of the wardens with one shoe in his hand he had been searching for his other shoe when the bomb exploded in his house, he was fast asleep, he was in a bad state of shock.

The Saturday night of the Merseyside Raid while I was staying with Dolly the German's bombed Edge-Hill railway station goods yard the whole place was on fire then they began showering bombs on Martindales coal yard it looked like a blazing furnace the whole sky was firey red and seeing Myrtle Gardens they may have thought it was a military base so they began to open fire again dropping loads and loads of more bombs, as the bombs were falling people were running down the stairs falling on top of one another trying to reach the air raid shelters it was a mad stampede, it went on till six o clock in the morning, about that time Dolly kept telling to hurry on home it wasn't like her I think she had a premonition, I didn't know what kind of a shock I was in for, as I walked across to our block of flats I stood transfixed to the ground as I looked up there was nothing there, except smoke and rubble and debris our house had been completely wiped out with the bombing can you imagine how I must have felt? I thought all of our family had been killed I was in such a state of shock my mind went blank when suddenly I heard me Dad calling me I thought I was dreaming all this I looked around there he was my guardian angel standing there he gave me a new lease of life, before I'd seen him I just wanted to die he told me that all of our family had survived they had been taken to St Saviour's school or church I can't remember which, they were all given medical treatment and rest with the homeless.

The same night of that air raid Mum and Dad had decided not to go down in to the shelter if they had gone down they would have been killed because all the people in the shelters had been killed or trapped to death, when they had been bombarded with bombs.

Mum got a piece of shrapnel in left hand she didn't make any fuss about it she was very brave caring for all her children was the most important thing to her. Later on when the flats had been repaired we went back there to live in the same house that had been bombed.

The Prime Minister Winston Churchill, spoke seriously on the radio advising all parents to let their children be evacuated to the country, as it would be much safer for them, with our haversacks on our back and a label attached to our coats with our names on it and our gas masks off we went from St Ann's school to the railway station, as our parents waved us goodbye some of us were crying we had never been away from home before the rest of us were excited for we had never been to the country it seemed like an adventure to us.

There was my two young sisters Mary and Vera and my brothers Jimmy and Tucker me being the eldest had been told by Mum to take great care of them and see that no harm came to them when we arrived at our destination Wrexham in North Wales all the Welsh folks were there to greet us then we were taken to a school and given refreshments, later we were told to sit down while our names were being called out, by who ever wished to foster us you can imagen how we felt at getting separated because not all of the Welsh folks had sufficient room to take in large families.

During all the commotion I lost my little sisters and brothers in the crowds I sat on the floor and began to cry, suddenly a St John's Ambulance man approached me he asked me why I was crying I looked up at him still trying to control my emotions and told him I had lost my brothers and sisters in the crowd hem asked me their names after I told him he went searching through the crowds eventually he found them for me.

A Welsh lady came up to us after she introduced herself to us she told us her name was Mrs Hughes she choose to take Tucker and Jimmy to foster, she lived in Princess Street and told us that we would always be welcome anytime to call at her home to see our brothers.

We were taken to our foster home and introduced to a very lovely Welsh lady whose name was Mrs Maud Wright who also lived in Princess Street she also told us that our brothers could always visit us in her home.

In the evening after we had settled in lo and behold who should come walking in but the St John's Ambulance man who had come to my assistance in the school in finding my sisters and brothers for me he was Mrs Wrights husband his name was Horace what a nice surprise it was to him when he saw that we were his foster children.

They had an only son whose name is Clifford he was a few years older than us he had a lovely dog named Don they also had a lodger named Walter.

Mrs Hughes had a son named Billy I cant' recall if she had any more children, I remember Billy's granddad he lived up in the Welsh mountains occasionally he came and spent weekends with them, he was a lovely story teller.

Sunday afternoon after we had all settled in our foster homes. One of the neighbours in Princess Street where some of our friends had gone to live invited us all out in his car to view the country side it was a lovely sunny afternoon with the roof top of his car open and the wide open spaces with not a care in the world singing to the top of our voices we had never seen such beautiful country side and all the lovely animals.

When we returned home after the glorious outing he took us into his tuck shop and gave us ice-cream lemonade and sweets, the mischief that we got up to innocently we plucked lovely flowers and we eat so much fruit it's a wander we weren't sick Mary my young sister plucked a lovely bunch of flowers from some one's garden she presented them to Mrs Wright saying "These are a present to you Mrs Wright was so delighted with the gesture and thanked her for them.

The following day Mr Wright was on his way to work when along came his boss as they went walking along his boss said to him "Some bloody little evacuees came and plucked up nearly all the flowers from our garden yesterday " Mr Wright replied "Those little evacuees are now my foster children " they both had a good laugh over the incident.

My young brother Jimmy tried to runaway he was homesick, he only stayed for a short period then he returned back home to Liverpool.

It must have been hard for Clifford having three adopted sisters he was very kind to us and his friend Ron Davies always brought us lovely home made savoury pies every Monday and Walter the lodger used to make us lovely cheery cake, we were well fed with lots of home grown fruit and vegetables from the allotments, it must have been very hard for Mrs Wright fostering three girls she never once complained,

Our bedroom was a shimmering pale green colour, on our dressing table there where lovely trinket sets, perfumed talcum powder and links of pretty beads and brooches from our bedroom window we could see straight across to the tuck-shop, all the evacuees that lived near by use to go there to buy sweets, bubbly-gum soft drinks and ice-cream etc.

In the kitchen where we had our first meal there was a lovely coal-fire where Mrs Wright did her cooking, I remember my first breakfast there it was Kellogs corn flakes and lots of fresh cows milk, home grown tomatoes with fresh crusty bread and butter, we didn't have all this at home for breakfast as it was too expensive for Mum to afford and times were very hard.

During the seasons of autumn and winter we would sit around the coal-fire in the kitchen either reading sewing or knitting Mrs Wright gave us butterscotch sweets that had chocolate in the centre then just before bedtime we would have a cuppa cocoa and some biscuits.

The three of us slept in a large bed each night Vera and Mary would ask me to sing them to sleep, that is if you could call it singing, their favourite song was a popular but a sad song

"Goodnight children everywhere
Your Mammy thinks of you tonight
Lay your head upon your pillow
Don't' be a kid or a weeping willow
Close your eyes and say a prayer
And surely you can find a kiss to spare
Although I'm far away I'm with you, night and day
Goodnight children everywhere.

Sung by the Forces sweetheart Vera Lynn.

After I had finished singing it we would all start crying, later on we would fall fast asleep.

Tucker still lived with Mrs Hughes after Jimmy had returned home after all he was only about six years of age he didn't like it there. Sometimes we went on ramble walks with our teacher and the class studying all the wildlife in the country seeing all the various animals being small children we didn't realise that a war was going on that was the reason why we had been evacuated living in the country was like a fairy tale to us.

We saw our first Robin Redbreast in Wrexham and the Cup and Saucer Waterfall, when the lake was ponds were frozen we all went sliding upon a sledge that Clifford had made for us, we were thrilled with delight when he gave it to us and the cries of excitement as we went sliding merrily down the hill. We played in the snow for hours and made a huge snowman, we were never sick it must have been the country air it was so pure and bracing. Saturday mornings we all went to the Mickey Mouse club it was held in the Odeon cinema in Wrexham. Before the show began we would all join in singing this song, I will try and memorise it, it went like this,

> *"Every Saturday morning where do we go*
> *Getting in to mischief oh dear no*
> *To the Mickey Mouse club with our badges on*
> *Every Saturday morning at the Odeon*
> *Before we cross a busy road we look both ways*
> *If a car's approaching we wait until its gone*
> *Every Saturday morning at the Odeon.*

That's all I can remember.

Living in Wrexham and although sometimes we would feel a bit homesick we had lots of activities to keep us occupied, it was early November the country side at that time was something that I had never experienced before so the homesick feeling gradually disappeared, the crisp pure snow looked just like a soft white velvet blanket covering all around it reminded me of a beautiful Christmas card.

We saw Gypsies on their sites and the grey smoke rising in to the air from inside their caravans all the wonderful scenery that God had created for us to behold.

One day I took Mary and Vera shopping to Chester we bought a small toy telephone for Jimmy and a toy bunny rabbit for our baby brother Tony, while we were browsing around the market I had lost my little sisters again they were afraid as they couldn't see me anywhere after what seemed like hours we found one another we hugged each other so much with gladness.

As Christmas was approaching in our cookery class at school I made a Christmas cake I presented it to Mrs Wright as a token of gratitude she was delighted with it Mary has a wonderful memory she told me that I received first prize for the best Christmas cake in the class.

Clifford and his friends Ronnie and Gavin bought a huge Christmas tree from Bircham Woods they put it in the parlour and we all decorated it it was such an enjoyable and memorial Christmas Mrs and Mr Wright made us a lovely Christmas party they invited all the evacuees in our street and Tucker and his pals Clifford played the piano and we all stood around singing carols suddenly there was a power cut some one held a torch for Clifford to be able to play there where candles lit everywhere.

It was beginning to get dark some one was knocking on the front door it was me Dad he had just got out of a taxi the train had been delayed and we were not expecting him it was a lovely surprise, we were over the moon after he had been given some refreshments he was singing and enjoying himself he would have easy made it on Broadway he was a song and dance man always the life and soul of a party.

During that time Mum was evacuated in Bangor in North Wales with our baby brother Tony they were staying in a head masters house and his wife Mum only stayed a few days she was too anxious about me Dad and elder brother and sister Frances.

After Christmas we began getting homesick I think the novelty had wore off truthfully I didn't mind living there as I prefer the country to live in and I felt the tranquillity in Wales. I dream of possessing a small cottage in Wales Grandy was a true born Welsh man I would love to visit where he was born one fine day.

Finally we returned home to Liverpool, the war was still going on but we had lots of wonderful memories of Wrexham to cherish of our war period being evacuated there with such loving kind foster parents and foster brother.

From Vera and Mary and Clifford for sharing with us especially for keeping the photograph which you took of us and lending it to me to have a copy made its over fifty years old we all look so happy on it also a million thanks to your Mum and Dad who showered us with such love and kindness and to Ron Davies and Gavin and all your friends once again many thanks for sheltering all the mischievous evacuees from Liverpool.

9

CHRISTMAS TIME

Ma Clayton was quite Victorian looking on the corner of the street where her mini tuck shop was stood a gas-lamp as you entered her shop a tiny bell would twinkle then she would appear from the back room dressed elegantly and wearing a head turbon.

My sister Frances told me that who ever was Ma Claytons' first customer on a Monday morning would be given a small trifle Frances said that she used to be the first customer until the novelty wore off with Frances. On the shelves where boxes of assorted sweets that cost a farthing or a half penny some for a penny, on the counter in small boxes where swissels, liquorice sticks, gob stoppers and small packets of sweet cigarettes, pretty heart shaped pastel coloured sweets with words wrote on them that said "I love you" we used to play games with them, there where trays of home made Holland toffee, banana split toffee, treacle toffee fudge aniseed balls bubbly gum spearmint and various chocolates. To serve the toffee she would break it up with a tiny hammer then put it in to a small paper bag and weigh it on the small brass scales, she also sold cigarettes and cigarette tobacco she sold pipe tobacco by the half ounce she would slice the pipe tobacco on a small wooden board with a special knife then weigh it on miniature brass scales and put tiny weights with the weight printed on them. She gave us tiny pieces of broken toffee for free.

From the beginning of September until Christmas Eve nearly all of the children joined Ma Claytons' Cadburys' Christmas club, it was a total of five shillings we would pay every week from our pocket money the rest was made up by doing chores also from the money we received from our relatives, she would issue us with a small pink club card and write down the payments then on Christmas Eve we would wait eagerly for me Dad to come home from work he would take us to Ma Claytons' to pay the balance of our sweet club for us, she would give us a lovely selection of Cadburys' assortments of milky ways, mars bars chocolate whirls rollos chocolate smarties marzipan bars and coconut slabs etc, we would have to save the selection until Christmas day.

As autumn evenings started to draw near we would sit around the dinning room table with Mum making Christmas decorations, she would buy a couple of packets of assorted pastel coloured crepe paper, and a small jar of glue as she showed us how to cut out medium size strips using our fingers and thumbs we would give it a gentle twist and create lovely decorations by joining them altogether making long chains of decorations we also made pretty paper lanterns.

We had a lovely aunty Mary and Uncle John they were well off financially, they were very kind to us they had four children Johnny Katheen Terry and Monica every Christmas they always took us to see a pantomime at the Pavilion in Lodge Lane, one Christmas as we were going to a pantomine I was walking day dreaming when suddenly, I started tapping on the spearmint machines, that where attached to walls in most of the streets, when you put a half penny in to the slot of the machine you got two packets, some of the kids would hide while another put a coin in they would count the number of coins that went in as soon as it came to the fourth turn they would all make a dash to the machine to get two packets there was always a big scramble for the machine.

This day as I was tapping on the machine suddenly dozens of

packets of spearmint kept coming out of the machine I was flabbergasted I rolled up my sweater to try and catch them all, there
were too many so I called my cousin Johnny to come and help me
he came running he couldn't believe his eyes the two of us were
laughing like mad. The man must have forgot to lock the
machine. We shared all the packets of spearmints with all the
kids, I never told me Mum she would have gone mad but it was
only innocent childish fun.

In school we would be preparing for Christmas, rehearsing a play
called "The Nativity" we also made calendars soft toys and pretty aprons etc.

We always went to the grotto in T J Hughes or Blacklers I think it
cost half a crown we would receive a small present from Santa
Claus, the girls presents were wrapped up in pink paper the boys
were wrapped up in blue inside they would be a small toy, the
children who were more well than us had their photograph taken
with Father Christmas.

Mum always joined in a clothes shop club in Paddington and a
provident club, the girls would have pretty velvet frocks in different colours, red blue green and gold we had black patent leather
ankle- band shoes and three quarter length white socks, the boys
all had new suits shirts sweaters socks etc, we always looked a
credit to Mum and Dad when we went to Christmas Mass.

Poor Mum she never had anything new we would save up to buy
her and me Dad a Christmas present we would all stand around
the kitchen table watching her preparing the Christmas and pudding and mince pies and her lovely Irish bunloaf after she had
mixed the pudding she would put a few six penny pieces in to the
mixture then we would all have a stir and make a wish it was a
very old tradition, after the cake had been baked she would it in
a large biscuit tin until it was time to decorate it, with marzipan

and icing sugar and cake decorations.

A week before Christmas Mum asked me to go to town with her on a message, I remember it was a large building, there where crowds of people there they were all poor with large families, there was no birth control pill during that period, when it came to our turn M um was given a large parcel it was called The Goodfellows Parcel It was distributed from some charity organisation, when we arrived home Mum opened the parcel it contained a large tin of ham mince meat sausages a tin of salmon a large packet of tea and sugar a Christmas cake and a Christmas pudding biscuits a large tin of fruit and fresh cream and a jelly.

On Christmas Eve Mum would go to the market just before closing time it was much cheaper then after we returned home, Dad would clean it and stuff it with sausage meat and sage and onions, and put it in a large roasting tin and roast it with dripping slowly in the oven, the aroma was lovely Mum would be in the back kitchen preparing the potatoes and vegetables, all the kids went carol singing, it was great fun we were so naïve some of us still believed in Father Christmas we were so excited telling one another what we wrote and asked him to bring us, after we had finished carol singing we had our tea, Dad went for his pint we had our bath and waited up for his return home we would have a lovely time he would sing all his favourite songs for us.

When I was a little girl we lived in Bancroft street near by the stables the house belonged to Gran O' Donnell one Christmas Eve Frances and me shared the same bed it was a four poster with brass nobs on top where we hung up our pillow slip for Santa Claus with a note pinned to it asking him what we wished him to bring us.

One Christmas morning I awoke very early to my surprise I saw a large box at my side of the bed I couldn't open it quick enough lying inside the box was a beautiful sleeping doll, I couldn't believe my eyes I thought I must have been dreaming until I gave Frances a nudge to wake her up to her surprise she also had a lovely sleeping doll inside of our pillow slips that we had hung were, apples tangerines chocolate nuts and some money, our brothers had boxes of toy soldiers toy drums books and harmonica's etc.

You could hear the cries of delight from us showing one another our presents, one Christmas- Eve some one in our family told us that they didn't believe in Santa Claus I wont' give them away Mum told them to be quiet, when that person awoke on Christmas morning all they received to their surprise was some cinders in a small bag Mum said to them "That's what you get for not believing in Santa, eventually they were given their presents, I saw me Mum give me Dad a smile it was so nostalgic. Even if it was only make believe try and guess who it was I suppose they thought they were too old for make believe. Mum's Christmas present would be a pretty pinafore or a glass milk jug and sugar basin Dad would get a pair of socks or a tie or hankies.

After our Christmas breakfast we would go to Mass wishing that we would have a white Christmas making it more real, kneeling down in church seeing the crib with baby Jesus lying in the Manger carrying their gifts, the shinning star of Bethlehem hanging in front of the crib, the beautiful coloured crystal glass window glass of the church, and the carols being sung walking home after mass we would be so happy telling our friends what we had got for Christmas like wise they would do the same all of us swanking in our new clothes.

Uncle Jim our favourite uncle would come to our house for Christmas he would greet us with "A Merry Christmas" then we would exchange presents with him Dad would carve the turkey as Mum prepared our dinner after dinner and Christmas pudding and custard we would play games.

After our lovely tea the girls would wash the dishes then the best part to follow was our concert, Uncle Jim would play his harmonica while Dad sang to us we would have tears in our eyes as he sang his favourite song called

"The Little Drummer Boy"

"He's the little boy that Santa Claus forgot
And goodness knows he didn't want a lot
He sent a note to Santa for some soldiers and a drum
He broke his little heart when he found Santa hadn't come
In the street he envied all the lucky boys
Then wandered home to last years broken toys
I feel sorry for that laddie he hasn't got a Daddy
The little boy that Santa Claus forgot.

Then it would be Mums' turn to give us a song, she had a lovely lilting sweet voice her favourite songs were Nellie Kelly Danny Boy and Three O Clock In The Morning.

Aunt Mary and Uncle John would come around and some more relations, they would have a holey dancing and singing merrily we would all join in.

For all the lonely and sick people who didn't have any family a charitable organisation would go to their home and give them a lovely Christmas dinner and a present. There was a lovely Christmas spirit all around, it wasn't commercialised there was a genuine excitement preparing for Christmas although folks were poor.

10
RETURN TO ROOTS

Lason and I lived in Aberdeen road in Highbury north London for three years the neighbours were caring and friendly people, they were of different nationalities and some very nice Gays who lived on both sides Rufus and Lawrence ran a guest house Lawrence was a clerk, on the right side lived Bernard and Harry they were both nurses in the hospital, all of the children loved Lason they used to sit on the front door step and the garden wall outside the house during the nice weather playing and talking along would come the ice-cream vendor and Lason would treat all of the children to an ice cream, even now sometimes when I hear the chimes of the ice cream van I recall those happy days.

Some of the courting couples and our friends used to come up to our flat Lason would entertain them with his records listening to soul and rock steady reggie ska and bluebeat, he had a good taste for music, he was a brilliant dancer his laugh was contagious they would sit and reason.

After living in that flat until (1968) our dream came true, we were given a new one bedroom flat to rent from the council it was unbelievable, it had central heating with a huge kitchen in the living room was a verandah that opened from the living door, all the children from Aberdeen road assisted us to take all. the small luggage over, it wasn't far from to walk to.

I remember one little boy he was always in trouble he wore one of

Lasons' hat, some one told us not to have there as he was a little thief we ignored them Lason seemed to be very fond of refreshments and as he was leaving he would give him some pocket money.

There was a lot of prejudiced in the sixties over mixed races being together sometimes it was very hard you just had to ignore it and leave it to peoples I remember a very dear friend of mine a titled lady Miss Ramsay said to me that a true Christian wouldn't behave in that way even some of the churches were hypocrites, you got it from many ranks which you wouldn't expect.

Lason and I lived together for twelve years we were married Brougham Terrace in Liverpool then we returned back to London. One autumn evening he said to me "If anything should happen to me promise me that you will go back home to Liverpool" I couldn't make out why he said that to me, except he must have had a premonition because I remember once saying to him that I would die if ever anything happened to him he hadn't long come back from his vacation in a Jamacia.

One winters morning in January about three o clock he became very ill we didn't have a telephone we were waiting for it to be installed, I became scared I thought he was going to have a heart attack I dressed him to take him to the hospital, as we came outside the snow was about six inches deep it looked like a thick snow white blanket not one spec on it, the moon was shinning it was bitterly cold and the wind was howling, I had to leave him in a doorway of a beauty salon that Pat owned Lason looked very ill he was freezing, as I buttoned his top coat right up I told him to stay in the doorway while I tried to find a taxi, I trudged down Highbury Hill to the taxi cab office it was closed, on account of the server weather, I was frantic I couldn't walk fast as the snow was too deep I was scared of falling, back up the hill I went walking in the middle of the road it was much harder coming back up and my feet were wet and I kept slipping down, it took me about half an hour to get back to Lason when I did he was shivering in the door way I put the collar of his coat right up then I began rubbing his hands his lips and hands to keep his blood circulating they were blue with the cold then I began to search all around for a cab there was not one insight I was bewildered.

I went to the corner of Highbury Grange where the paper lady stands early each morning there was not a soul in sight I stood there for ages, it was getting on to four o clock now, more snow began to fall suddenly, from out of nowhere I saw a taxi coming towards Highbury Barn I shouted and hailed it thank God it stopped I helped Lason in to it then I told the driver our destination, he took the longest way round I was furious but this was no time to argue finally we arrived at the London hospital in Whitechapel, even inside the hospital it was quite cold at least we felt safer and warmer than hanging about in the street anxiously trying to find a cab.

After given some of the details to the nurse in the causality we waited for ages for the doctor to arrive, he took Lason in to a cubicle I stood outside of the cubicle listening as the Doctor examined him, Lason then told him that his G P. told him that he had rheumatism and showed him the medication that he had prescribed this Doctor told him that he would like him to go to the Cardiac department immediately the next day, we went the next morning he was given tests after the results he was told that he was to be admitted in to hospital as soon as a bed was vacant.

In early February he was admitted into Mile-End hospital, the consultant told him that he had thrombosis and he needed a minor operation. The operation was not a success they said he would have to have another operation I refused to sign for it was far too soon after his first one and I thought that if ever anything happened to him I could never forgive myself, during that period while I was visiting Lason I noticed a large Union Jack flag on the wall in the ward he was in it was a bit strange to me because no royalty or distinqished people had been on a tour to the hospital, my mind was quite clear I was very much aware of all that was happening.

My Niece Margaret and her husband came from Liverpool to visit their Uncle I remember mentioning to Margaret and Frank about the Union Jack flag at that time they were more shocked and concerned about his welfare.

I remember one evening while I was visiting Lason I was sitting on a bench waiting to enter the ward when I got friendly with a lady who was visiting her husband she told me that her husband had been in hospital for two months and tat he had contacted a bug during his stay, she had to wear a plastic gown and plastic covers on her feet and a mask to cover her face and mouth before she entered the private cubicle he was in, she told me that so far they didn't have a cure for the bug, they didn't know what caused it. Later on some person brought the bug in to the ward that Lason was in visitors were informed that their relatives were to be isolated upstairs, I was not notified so I asked to see Lason's Consultant after much persuasion I saw her I asked her what the bug was that he had caught she replied that she could have it or I could have it, I said how would I know she said by your urine, and still so far they had no cure for it.

I kept thinking about the Union Jack Flag in the ward and the National front as they were very racist to black folks and some of them worked in the hospital, Lason was Jamaican and I am white and they opposed to mixed marriages if I'm wrong then I apologies but if not, what was a large Union Jack flag doing on the wall in the ward? As I continue my true story it gets a lot more questioning, I had to phone one morning and ask the ward sister if Lason could have a blanket bath I was a nurse myself in my teen years so I knew all about nursing and hygiene some of the nursing staff treated him unfairly there was nothing I could do to prevent it as it would have made it worse for him.

They transferred all the patients upstairs to another ward as their ward had to be fumigated I went early the next morning and I sat where I could not be seen, I watched as one of the nursed took Lason upstairs on a wheel chair in the lift I followed up the stairs she didn't know that I was behind her she just dropped him down in to a bed like a rag doll with only one pillow he could hardly breathe, I went up to her in the office and politely asked her if I could have a pillow for my husband she asked me his name when I told her his name she threw the pillow at me I was shocked by her attitude after I had been visiting him sometimes, I would have to clean his locker and dispose of his surgical dressings and empty bottles, etc this is the Gods truth.

The second operation they performed on him without my knowledge or my consent I was totally shocked when I visited him that evening, he was in a private ward he hadn't come round yet they were giving him a blood transfusion also he was on a drip, I asked to see his consultant he took me in to his office I asked him to kindly explain to me exactly what they were doing to Lason He drew a diagram showing me all that had happened to poor Lason he wanted to operate on him again and amputate his leg, I remember sobbing and saying to him "You are killing him, this will be his death I refused point blankly for them to operate on him again. I looked at Lason as he was trying to come round but he looked Like he had lost the will to live.

One afternoon while I was visiting him the orderly was giving out cups of tea in plastic tea cups, on account of the bug being contagious Lason asked me why the plastic cups I said it was easier for them to dispose of and save the washing up it was just to stop him from wondering why.

That night he kept telling me to go home I couldn't understand why as I left I was walking along the corridor I glanced back to look at him, he was sitting cropped up in bed all the patients were having their supper he seemed to be miles away I couldn't fathom it out on (March 14th) I went to St Joan of Arc's church to ask the priest to pray for Lason, when I arrived home I felt exhausted I lay down on the settee and fell in to a deep sleep I had a dream I dreamt that Lason was standing over me smiling it felt so real suddenly I heard myself saying "Lason stop making me laugh" suddenly the door bell rang I got up to answer it there stood a policeman he told me that I was wanted at the hospital immediately, I arrived at the hospital I was ushered in to the sisters office she told me that Lason had passed away, I was absolutely stunned I couldn't speak or even utter a sound I just froze inside me, I asked to see him.

He was already laid out he looked so peaceful no more pain and suffering I remember saying to him. "I'm sorry that I wasn't hear to hold your hand and say farewell to you before you passed on". As I said before I was once a nurse and the procedure has always been if a patient was dying you notified their next of kin why wasn't I notified it has always been a mystery to me but you will find out before the conclusion.

Margaret my niece came from Liverpool to assist me with the funeral arrangements we went to Leytonstowe to choose Lasons' resting place it was a private plot, the sun was shinning although it was bitterly cold and a few snow flakes began to twirl around to the ground, there was a school near by we could hear the children' voices and laughter as they were playing it must have been their break we picked a spot right by the church, Margaret that he would love it there as he loved being with children he was like the Pipe Piper if they had any problems they went to him for advice.

Lason was buried on ST Patricks day (March 17th) it was a very long way to Leyonstowe, there where a few more cars following behind us we had to cross a long bridge then a round a bout, brother Keith and brother Stewart were following behind Margaret and Frank then Ronnie and Danny, we kept going around in circles so a patrol car passed Margaret asked the police man the way as we had lost trace of the under taker he must have took a shorter route it was hilarious really although it was a funeral by now we were getting anxious, thinking that we would be late eventually we arrived, again as we entered the cemetery snow flaked began to fall they melted with the sun although it was a bitterly cold day.

Two months after Lason had passed away I phoned the administrator of the hospital after giving him all the details I asked to arrange an appointment for me to see Lasons' consultant, he sounded so sympathetic and fixed an appointment for me.

In the meantime I had wrote down all the medical questions with the assistance of my friend Tetla who is a qualified private nurse, the day of the appointment I went along with Miss Ramsay, we were invited in to a small room not long after the consultant entered with his secretary as we sat down I saw him glance at my note book in my hand, first I asked him why I wasn't notified about Lason contacting the bug of which they couldn't find a cure for he replied that it was just a red hering then his secretary repeated his same words, she was just supposed to be there to tale notes, she wasn't medical staff secondly I asked him who signed for Lason's second operation without my consent he replied that Lason had signed I then asked to see his signature when he showed me the signature it was Lasons' but it was so scribbled remember he was heavily sedated so he wasn't in his proper frame of mind and it was far too soon for them to operate on him after his first operation, while this debate was going on Miss Ramsay kept silent all the way through suddenly she interrupted she said to the consultant, why wasn't Mrs Richards notified when her husband was dying? Because you knew he wouldn't survive he replied that it was too much of a shock for the medical team.

I said to him Lason was a very strong person only(44 years) of age that he only came in for a minor operation yet he had two operations in just six weeks he deterriated yet still you wanted to perform a third operation to amputate his leg that I had definitely refused you to do his secretary still kept interrupting I was beginning to get annoyed I thought to myself it wasn't her next of kin who had been neglected.

After we left the hospital we took a cab to Miss Ramsay's house her maid Mabel served us tea Miss Ramsay then said to me "Oh dear Bridie I'm so sorry that things didn't go well for us today with Lasons' consultant by taking proceedings against their negligence but at least you have helped other people because they will be far more careful in future, she was not a lady who minced her words.

I told her about an incident that happened with Lason before he passed away after he was taken back down to the first ward again where the Union Jack flag was on the wall. One night a patient in the next bed to Lason was very ill he kept calling out for the nurse to come to his aid, unfortunately he was just ignored by then early hours in the morning, he passed away Lason blew his top he told the nurse off for not coming to the patent in his request for help, the same day I went in to visit him he told me the whole story I went and apologised to the nurse on his behalf as he looked scared strange but true Lason passed away a few days later with not a blessing from a friend yet God was with him for who did we bump in to visiting a patent but Miss Ramsays neighbour who was a vicar she asked me if I would like him to bless Lason the two of us knelt as he blessed Lason Union Jack flag in the ward.

I packed up all my belongings and returned back home to Liverpool it was a traumatic upheaval Margaret Frances and Danny were waiting to welcome me home. I rented a flat in Alexandra Drive near Lark Lane, sometimes I felt scared and lonely and I missed my friends.

One Saturday morning in September I decided to go to Paddy's market it was years since I last went there, the sun was just beginning to break through there was a nip in the air branches from the trees and leaves were scattered and blackcurrants on a small branch lay upon the ground after the fierce gales in the night there was not a soul in sight it was quite early in the morning the best part of the day for me,

There was a peaceful atmosphere all around I caught a bus to Cazenue street and got off at St Anthony's church and walked through the ally way to the market.

I rummaged about for a pair of winter boots no luck, upon the ground where a Mary Ellen stood by her pitch I saw two lovely pink woollen jumpers good as new nice and snuggy to keep out the winter chills they only cost sixty pence, I heard a hawker shouting out great winter boots going cheap, I approached his stall and found a pair of black knee length winter boots that I bought for only ten pounds.

On my way home I went in to St Anthony's church and lit a candle for all the dear departed souls, the candles were flickering it looked like a grotto yet, even when people opened the doors to enter they never blew out, outside flowers were blooming birds were chirping merrily as spring was in sight.

The reason that I returned to Liverpool was I had made a solemn promise to Lason when he asked me that if ever anything should ever happen to him I would return back home to my roots, he must have had a premonition that he was going to die, he was a very philosophical person.

That was a great decision for me to make after living in London all those years where I had such loving and caring friends, life is so strange we question it, sometimes its like The Windmill Of The Gods.

One lovely sunny August afternoon I decided to go and view Myrtle Gardens, down memory lane for old times sake, try and visualize this folks had lived there during the (1939) during that period the corporation flats were rented to the working class folks for a few shillings a week, most were families and a few childless couples now they have been modernised in to self contained luxury flats, they must cost around thirty to forty thousands pounds to buy majority of the occupants are civil servants or people on a very high income, they are now called Myrtle Court it so nostalgic for me after all those years, the first thing I noticed was it was summer time during the school holidays yet, there was not a single sign of any children romping about, no cries of delight it seemed strange to me I thought of the bad days and the good days when we were children living there, then I remembered all the people who had been killed in the war, all the shops had been demolished where they once stood now there where trees and grass and lots of wild flowers.

As I approached the house where we had once lived in which all the Thomas family had been killed during the war, inside of the front room on the window sill stood a large plant and some small plants in pots up at the bedroom window hung curtains.

Next door where Gran O' Donnell used to live there was also a large plant pot on the window sill in the living room in the bedroom there hung beige coloured velvet curtains.

Across the way in Neville Place on the corner where the snug room used to be where I used to go for Ganny's wee drop of whiskey there where trees grass and more wild flowers growing all around I paused for a while picturing and thinking that if Ganny was here now she would have sat here by the tree with her dog Prince by her side sipping her wee dram of whiskey, watching the world go by.

Where Mrs Smith used to stand by her stall selling her potatoes, vegetables fruit and flowers on a Saturday and Sunday, serving all the neighbours.

I saw daisies and dandelions growing all along the pavements the branches of the trees were swaying with the gentle breeze as the sun was shinning down upon them.

I'm still on tour in Myrtle Gardens your not allowed inside there is a security guard on the gate, after I had shown him my credentials and told him that I had lived there when I was a little girl he was quite pleasant and allowed me in to browse and take notes.

At the main entrance written in gold Italic letters is Myrtle Court Near by the lodge there's another sign saying

"WILL ALL VISITORS
PLEASE REPORT TO THE SECURITY–LODGE"

The swings are no longer there where I had lost Mums rent money while I was happily swinging away on the swinging boat it brought it all back to me.

There's another bronze iron gate then there's more trees and wild flowers in the middle of the ground stands a beautiful bronze statue, the staircase has a glass cover.

As I stood admiring the view a beautiful Indian lady dressed in a orange satin sari wearing beaded brown leather sandals her jet black hair adorned with a pearl comb and golden bracelets on her wrist walking gracefully by, smiled at me we both greeted each other good day.

Quite a few people passed by they were of different races, the police bridal that used to be on the corner of Orphan street had been demolished on the corner of Lully street where Delia's fruit shop had been and Garrets grocer's shop and Dave's tuck shop in Myrtle street and Slaters fish and chip shop and Irvins shop all once stood they had all long vanished.

Butterflies are dancing all around me I feel as If I'm living in the past, in fairy tale world I pluck a bunch of wild flowers to take home with me and place in a vase I planted a few cuttings to put in our front garden down stairs they are still growing each time I look out of my window and see them I remember my childhood.

During the (1930's) most married women still wore Mary Ellen shawls as little girls the majority of us would baby mind while our Mums worked with diligence. Mum would pass the baby to me then she would wrap her Mary Ellen shawl around the baby and me I would be made up imagining that I was a grown up lady.

Such a strange coincidence that day I went on the tour down memory lane while I was picking some wild flowers from the grass I spotted a small card with a picture of a young girl with a baby in her arms, hugging her close to her bosom her hair was dressed in Edwardian style she was wearing a Mary Ellen shawl around her shoulders to keep the baby warm.

As I made my departure I glanced up to (50 c) to the house where we were bombed out of, during the blitz it had been re-modernised in to luxury flats secured with iron railings and security alarms. Where Martindales coal-yard once stood now there where lock up garages.

On a Monday morning in (August 22 end 1994) I went to visit Gran O' Donnell's resting place, she was buried in a paupers grave people could not afford a decent burial during her time, while I waited for the bus to arrive a gentle breeze began to blow, when I arrived at my destination I went in to a fruit shop and bought two bunches of flowers and foliage, I asked the shop assistant if she would fill the two glass jars with water for me, as I entered the cemetery gates the sun began to appear I saw two workmen one was gathering a large bunch of grass while the other one was driving a tractor, I approached the man with the bundle of grass in his hands and asked him if he could assist me to find Ganny's resting place as it was years since I had last been there, he told me that "Five hundred pauper graves had all been demolished and that a grass lawn had been paves over it gave me quite a shock as I had been longing to go and place my flowers on her grave, he walked with me cross the green lawn and showed me where, Mum's grave was I thanked him he returned back to work.

I took out a bouquet of flowers and some foliage arranged them in a jar of water and placed them on the resting place of Mum and my brother Gerry, I lingered for a while thinking how much I missed them and Tony my younger brother who had been cremated, then I walked slowly across the lawn to where Gran O' Donnell had been buried, the sun was scorching hot, I sat down on the grass trying hard to search for a clue, to where she could be buried now, I was feeling so very sad at not being able to find her burial place, there where about three soldiers graves with headstones one had been killed in action another headstone of a young lad whose name was Bernard Thomas aged eighteen years of age died (1945) so I took out the glass jar with water and the bouquet of flowers and arranged them in the jar then I placed the jar by his headstone, I don't think his family would object to my gesture.

I sat down again on the grass by the wall where Ganny had first been buried there was nothing there only grass I took off my jacket laid it down with my bag upon the grass I kept trying to picture where her grave could be, I started to cry talking to her spirit saying "Oh Ganny I can't find where you are sleeping I could hear the birds chirping, the sky was a lovely pale blue I looked up at the fluffy blue and white clouds then at the trees, and the wide open space it was so peaceful I wanted to stay there all afternoon unfortunately I couldn't after sitting there for about an hour I got up looked all around the grass lawn where all the pauper graves had once been, I plucked a few wild flowers buttercups daisies and dandelions and some fern from the spot where my Ganny's grave had once been I took the flowers home with me as a last memory I felt a very deep loss for her I really missed her especially more now that her grave had vanished. A large black butterfly covered with beautiful coloured dotes flew across my face then, another lovely yellow one flew by I picked a few large weather cones lying beneath the trees that had fallen on to the ground I felt so tuned in with nature all around it felt so nostalgic, I put the cones in my bag and the ribbon from the flowers then I headed for home.

I made enquiries to the council asking why weren't we notified about the graves being getting demolished? They weren't very helpful so I did some research in the library this is what I found.

(16 February 1986) *Catholic Pictorial*

BIGGEST CLEAN UP YET

Jungle high grass obscuring gravestones gives way to neat clean lawns and a dignified appearance. The biggest renovation in the (128 years) history of Catholic cemeteries is under way in the archdiocese.

Already major changes have been made at Yew Tree and Ford cemeteries and work is still going on.

Following the imitation of an improvement programme by Mgr James Dunne and Fr Michael Mc Kenna Episcopal Vicar for Finance and Development, Mr Walter Withey, appointed Cemeteries Manager in (1984), got things underway.

Up to the summer of that year, Ford and Yew Tree Cemeteries were in a poor state of repair, Mr Whithey told the Pictorial. There were two main reasons for this, lack of money needed to maintain them properly and vandalism.

It was distressing for relatives attending funerals and visitors attending graves clearly firm action had to be taken to put things right.

Selected areas of Ford and Yew Tree were landscaped and turfed in line with general practise everywhere borderstones were removed and paved areas transformed into lawns.

Some public reaction was hostile said Mr Whithey. People who had complained about the state of the cemeteries, now turned their anger on the administration who were trying to restore the cemeteries to their former glory.

It was difficult to explain to people exactly what the operation would achieve and (most were against it).

As work progressed and the cemeteries were clearly

looking much better, the hostility dwindled and most people seemed pleased with the results except me because I still don't know where Ganny has been moved to.

In fact said Mr Withey, people are now worried because some sections haven't been landscaped yet but they will be in time he assures.

Eventually all the cemeteries will be completely restored and we ask every one to bear with us until the work has been finished Mr Withey says.

If everything goes according to our plan then all Catholics will see that our Archdiocese has cemeteries we can be proud of.

The paupers' graves had no headstones, grass grew upon them folks had no jobs they couldn't afford to buy a private grave.

It still is not fair why we the next of kin of the deceased were not notified that our relatives graves were to be demolished, why weren't we notified?

This is where my Grandmother was buried, in a pauper grave that has now disappeared.

Yew Tree Cemetery
Section A
Grave No.(1150)

The folks that were buried there are;

John Cullen address unknown.
Michael Arthur Sullivan, he lived in Mill street Liverpool 8.

Annie Brody. She lived in Belmont road Liverpool
Katherine Mc Donough who lived in Carter street Liverpool 8.
Bridget Jones from 19 A. Myrtle Gardens. Liverpool 7.

Bridget Jones my Ganny was the last person to be laid down to rest in that pauper grave. Ganny was (79 years) of age when she passed away on (13-6-1940).

I forgot to mention that our little friend the boy who we were told was a rouge came to offer me his condolences when Lason passed away wearing his cadet uniform he had turned out to be a proper gentleman Lason would have been so proud of him. There is a saying that says

PROVERB
Do not judge a man
Until you've walked two moons, in his moccassions.

Miss Ramsay was a titled lady with an M.B.E. she was known to lots of folks many of different races and also in many towns and especially in the east end of London where they named her "The Second Florence Nightingale" for all her devoted work they named a street after her called Ramsay street in the east end of London.

I remember accompanying her one summer afternoon in Whitechapel the two of us carrying large cane baskets filled with groceries that we distributed to some poor folks, all that came out of her own pocket.

She got a pharmacist banned from selling metholated spirits to alcoholics, they used to hang out on the bombed site in Montaque street completely blind drunk out of their senses majority of them had served in the war and in the Foreign Legion, just around the corner was The Salvation Centre where she would send them to be cared for.

No matter if it was day or night people who were desperate for assistance would always be welcome in her home.

When she was a young student doing a survey on the homeless she went to stay in a lodging house for a week, you had to pay a few coppers for a bed and first you joined a long queue from about seven o clock in the evening.

One of the wardens noticed what lovely smooth hands she had, and said to her "I don't think you have done any step-flagging her time and devotion to helpless people was endless, one day her and Princess Alexandra opened a cyrpt in Spitalfields for the alcoholics, their story was published in the East End Advertiser.

My dearest loving friend Miss Edith Ramsay was always there for me one day she phoned me and invited me to see her, when I arrived she asked me to read her will, that she had just completed typing I was astounded she had left large sums of money to various charities, eventually she was admitted to a private nursing home after having a serious accident she was now ninety two years of age and not capable of caring for herself, I went to visit her I felt sad her memory had failed she passed away not long after my visit to her. Gone but not forgotten by so many people that loved her, life is so precious and time flies by so fast.

At last I am coming to the conclusion of my true story it contains the absolute truth there may be a few errors over family ancestry I do hope that those who read it will enjoy it.

AS YE SOW
SO SHALL YE REAP

Printed in the United Kingdom
by Lightning Source UK Ltd.
118957UK00001B/52-72